SYSTEMS
SCIENCE LEVEL FOUR

P9-CST-672

Science Notebook

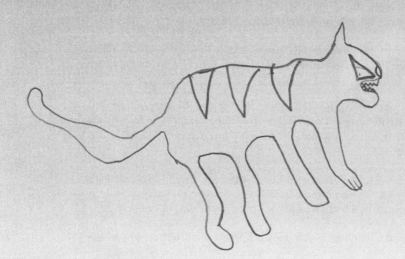

purposeful design
publications
A Division of ACSI

Colorado Springs, Colorado

© 2007 by ACSI/Purposeful Design Publications

All rights reserved. No portion of this book may be reproduced, stored in a retrieval system, or transmitted, in any form or by any means—mechanical, photocopying, recording, or otherwise—without prior written permission of ACSI/Purposeful Design Publications.

Purposeful Design Publications is the publishing division of the Association of Christian Schools International (ACSI) and is committed to the ministry of Christian school education, to enable Christian educators and schools worldwide to effectively prepare students for life. As the publisher of textbooks, trade books, and other educational resources within ACSI, Purposeful Design Publications strives to produce biblically sound materials that reflect Christian scholarship and stewardship and that address the identified needs of Christian schools around the world.

References to books, computer software, and other ancillary resources in this series are not endorsements by ACSI. These materials were selected to provide teachers with additional resources appropriate to the concepts being taught and to promote student understanding and enjoyment.

Unless otherwise identified, all Scripture quotations are taken from the Holy Bible, New International Version® (NIV®), © 1973, 1978, 1984 by International Bible Society. All rights reserved worldwide. The "NIV" and "New International Version" are trademarks registered in the United States Patent and Trademark Office by International Bible Society. Use of either trademark requires the permission of International Bible Society.

GORE-TEX® is a trademark of W. L. Gore and Associates, which does not sponsor, authorize, or endorse this textbook.
Silly Putty® is a registered trademark of Binney & Smith, used with permission.
STYROFOAM® is a trademark of the Dow Chemical Company, which does not sponsor, authorize, or endorse this textbook.
TEFLON® is a trademark of E. I. du Pont de Nemours and Company, which does not sponsor, authorize, or endorse this textbook.

Printed in the United States of America
16 15 14 13 12 11 10 09 08 07   1 2 3 4 5 6 7

Science, level four
Purposeful Design Science series
ISBN 978-1-58331-218-6   Science Notebook   Catalog #7516

Purposeful Design Publications
A Division of ACSI
PO Box 65130 • Colorado Springs, CO 80962-5130
Customer Service: 800/367-0798 • Website: www.acsi.org

Name _____

A Closer Look

Living things are made of cells. Examine three kinds of cells under a microscope. Draw what you observe.

Type of cell	Observations
Plant	
Amoeba	
Human Cheek	

1. How are these three types of cells similar? _____

_____

_____

_____

2. How are these three types of cells different? _____

_____

_____

_____

Name _____

What is in your mattress?

It is a gross, but true fact: tiny organisms called dust mites live in people's mattresses! That is not the only place they live. Dust mites make their homes in pillows, sofas, carpets, and any place dust can be found. Because they are so tiny, you can only see them with the help of a microscope. Dust mites hatch from eggs and live for about 30 days.

Dust mites feed on the dead skin cells of humans and animals. For this reason, they usually live in places where people live. When food supplies run low, dust mites will move to another place by attaching to a person's clothing. They have special skin cells that allow them to get the water they need by absorbing moisture from the air. If the air moisture level is too low for a long period of time, dust mites will cluster together to survive. By clustering together as a group, they conserve water.

How do you know that dust mites are alive? Use information found in the paragraphs above to complete the chart.

Dust mites are living things because they...	
acquire materials and energy	
develop and reproduce	
respond	
adapt	
are made of cells	

The next time you get in bed, think about all the tiny creatures you are sharing it with!

Name _____

Is yeast alive?

Yeast is a common ingredient in the kitchen. It helps breads and other baked goods to rise. Is yeast a living or nonliving thing? To answer this question, you will investigate whether yeast demonstrates the five characteristics of life. Each experiment poses a different question for investigation. After each experiment, circle your answer to the question.

EXPERIMENT #1: Does yeast acquire materials?   **YES NO MAYBE**

	Bottle Contents	Observations
Green	**Yeast** in warm water	
Yellow	**Sugar** in warm water	
Red	**Yeast and sugar** in warm water	

Summarize your observations: _____

_____

_____

Yeast is a fungus. Like many other organisms, it consumes sugar for food. Yeast then releases carbon dioxide. We can detect if carbon dioxide is released by observing the balloon. If the balloon expands, gas is being released similar to when we blow up a balloon.

What indicates that the yeast was using the sugar for food?

_____

_____

Name _____

EXPERIMENT #2: Does yeast respond to its environment?   **YES   NO   MAYBE**

Temperature changes in the environment are common. If yeast responds to its environment, changing the temperature may affect the yeast.

	Bottle Contents	Observations
Red	Yeast and sugar in **cold** water	
Red	Yeast and sugar in **warm** water	
Red	Yeast and sugar in **hot** water	

Summarize your observations:_____

_____

How does the yeast react to different temperatures?_____

_____

EXPERIMENT #3: Does yeast adapt to extreme temperatures? **YES   NO   MAYBE**

In general, yeast survives easily at mild temperatures. Can yeast survive extreme cold or heat?

	Bottle Contents	Observations
Blue	**Regular** yeast and sugar in warm water	
Orange	**Frozen** yeast and sugar in warm water	
Pink	**Baked** yeast and sugar in warm water	

Summarize your observations:_____

_____

Why does the yeast react differently?_____

_____

Name _____

Is yeast alive? (continued)

EXPERIMENT #4: Is yeast made of cells? **YES   NO   MAYBE**

Yeast is a microscopic organism. Use the microscope to examine the yeast. Draw what it looks like in the circle.

Summarize your observations: _____

_____

What does it look like the yeast is made of? _____

_____

EXPERIMENT #5: Does yeast develop and reproduce?   **YES   NO   MAYBE**

Notice how many cells you observe. Draw what you see through the microscope.

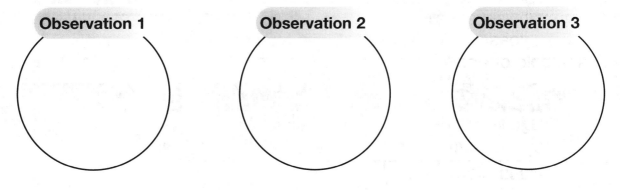

Summarize your observations: _____

_____

_____

Did the number of yeast increase, decrease, or stay the same? _____

_____

Name _____

Conclusions: Yeast Experiments

Indicate whether you think the following statements are **true**, **false**, or you do **not** have **enough evidence** to judge. Explain how your observations support your answers.

1. Yeast acquires materials and energy. ○ **True**   ○ **False**   ○ **Not enough evidence**

_____

2. Yeast develops and reproduces. ○ **True**   ○ **False**   ○ **Not enough evidence**

_____

3. Yeast responds.   ○ **True**   ○ **False**   ○ **Not enough evidence**

_____

4. Yeast adapts.   ○ **True**   ○ **False**   ○ **Not enough evidence**

_____

5. Yeast is made of cells.   ○ **True**   ○ **False**   ○ **Not enough evidence**

_____

Use the evidence you presented above to evaluate the following statement:
Yeast is alive.

○ **Yes**   ○ **No**   ○ **Not enough information**

Explain your reasoning.

_____

_____

_____

_____

_____

Name _____

Ant Observation

Procedure

1. Observe an ant farm for four days.
2. Identify two of the characteristics of living things that ants demonstrate and write about your observations.

Observation 1: ○ acquire materials and energy   ○ develop and reproduce
                    ○ respond   ○ adapt   ○ made of cells

Date _____

_____

_____

_____

Observation 2: ○ acquire materials and energy   ○ develop and reproduce
                    ○ respond   ○ adapt   ○ made of cells

Date _____

_____

_____

_____

Conclusions

1. Which characteristics of living things were you able to observe? _____

_____

_____

2. What else did you learn about ants? _____

_____

_____

Name _____

I want to learn more about ants.

Do some research! See what you can find out about ants.

1. Name some different kinds of ants. _____

_____

2. How long do ants live? _____

_____

3. What are the stages in an ant's life cycle? _____

_____

4. Describe ways that ants respond to their environment. _____

_____

_____

5. Describe some harsh conditions that ants can live through. _____

_____

_____

6. How do ants communicate? _____

_____

_____

My Sources
List the websites or books you used to find your information.

_____

_____

_____

Name _Garin Andrews #2 1V4/09_

Vocabulary Review

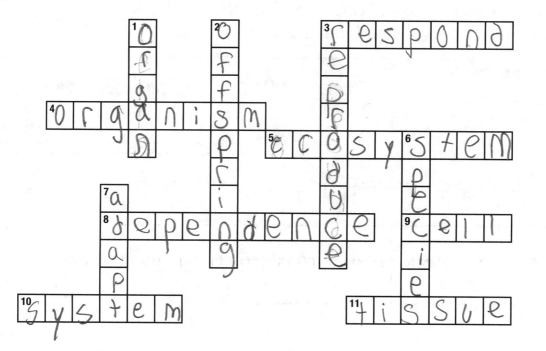

Across

3 To react to a stimulus
4 A living thing
5 A community of organisms and the nonliving things that make up the surroundings
8 A relationship in which an organism needs something else in order to survive
9 The basic building block of living things
10 A group of parts that work together to perform a task
11 A group of cells functioning together

Down

1 Two or more different kinds of tissues functioning together
2 A new organism produced by one or more parents
3 To produce offspring
6 A group of similar organisms that can mate and produce offspring that can also reproduce
7 To adjust routine behavior

© *Purposeful Design Science, Level Four* • Design of Life

Name _Garrin Andrews #2 11/5/09_

Chapter 1 Review

List the five characteristics of living things. Choose an organism and then give examples that demonstrate that it is a living thing.

Characteristics of Living Things	I know a _Snake_ is alive because it…
1. _acquire energy_	_It sneaks around and acquire food to eat like mice. It lays eggs, and it mite bite or slither away when some thing gets near it. It will move away if it's home get destroyed and they are made of cells._
2. _develop and reproduce_	
3. _respond_	
4. _adapt_	
5. _are made of cells_	

Fill in the blanks to show the organization of life: cell → _tissue_
→ _organ_ → organ system → _organism_ →
population → _community_ → ecosystem → _biospere_

A _or System tem_ is a rule that helps us to identify patterns seen throughout nature.
A living thing consisting of more than one cell is _tissue_ .

Name _____

Similarities and Differences

1. Look closely at the animals pictured on the cards. Consider the size of each animal. Sort the cards into three different groups—small, medium, and large. Write the names of the animals in the appropriate column.

Small	Medium	Large

2. Into which group would you place an animal card with a picture of a full-grown house cat?

_____

3. Look at the animal cards and study the characteristics of each animal. Do you see similarities and differences? Based on similarities, sort the animals into two or more groups. Draw and label a column for each group. Write the name of each animal in the appropriate column.

4. Into which of the groups would you place an animal card with a picture of a full-grown house cat?

_____

Name _Garvin Andrews_

Similarities and Differences, continued

Consider the groups below.

Group 1	Group 2	Group 3
gecko	wolf	mouse
macaw	beta fish	blacktip shark
snowshoe hare	alligator	bass
	vulture	hummingbird
		rattlesnake

5. What do the animals in Group 1 have in common?

They acen all walkers

6. Into which group would you place an animal card with a picture of a full-grown house cat? Explain your reasoning.

Group 2 there all aggressive

7. What specific characteristic was used to group the animals in this way?

They are all different species

Name Gavin Andrews

Mystery Creature

Look at the creature below. Write its description. Answer the questions and explain your answers.

Describe the creature's body, face, legs, hands, feet, ears, and anything else you notice.

Compare the size of the creature to the size of a quarter.

Description: It's body is small and furry, it's eyes are big and shiny, it's nose is very small

1. Where do you think it lives? Why? In the rainforest, Because He's hands are sticky

2. What do you think it eats? Why? Insects and leaves because it looks like a small frog and it lives in a tree

3. Do you think it hatches from an egg or is born live? Why? Born live. Because it has fur

Name _____

Compare Creatures

Look at the three organisms below and read their descriptions. Compare the mystery creature to each organism and answer the questions.

Tree frog	Bat	Lemur

- Lives in rain forest trees
- Eats insects
- Hatches from an egg

- Lives in trees or caves
- Eats insects and some fruits
- Born live

- Lives in trees
- Eats leaves, insects, fruit
- Born live

1. Compare body plans. How is the mystery creature similar?

Tree frog: _They both climb_

Bat: _It has it's ears, it nose, they eat the same thing are born live_

Lemur: _It has its eyes and its fur, a_

After comparing, your ideas may have changed. Answer these questions again.

2. Where do you think the mystery creature lives? Why? _forest Because it looks like it lives their_

3. What do you think it eats? Why? _nuts, Because it seems it could be related to a lemer._

4. Do you think it hatches or is born live? Why? _born live, Because it has fur_

Classify the mystery creature.

5. With which of these organisms would you classify the mystery creature? Why? _The lemur, Becaus they look a like_

Name _____

Mystery Creature Revealed

Use your previous answers and the paragraph provided by your teacher to answer the questions.

1. After comparing it to similar creatures, did any of your ideas about the

tarsier change? Why or why not? _____

_____

_____

_____

2. Did you classify the tarsier with the lemur? Why or why not? _____

_____

_____

_____

3. What did you learn about the tarsier by reading the paragraph? _____

_____

_____

_____

_____

_____

Name _____

Taxonomists Classify Organisms

Read the paragraph and answer the questions.

A group of taxonomists must identify a new organism. They will use a classification system that is based on the following criteria: body plans, development, habitats, and acquiring materials. First, they consider its body plan and place the new organism into a group with similar body plans. Then, within this group, they consider development and place the organism in a group that develops in the most similar way. Next, they consider habitat and place the organism in a group with others that share similar habitats. Last, they consider how the organism acquires materials. They separate those that acquire similar materials and place the new organism in this group. The taxonomists now have a group, including the new organism, that has similar body plans, development, habitats, and acquired materials. After comparing it to others, the organism is identified, classified, and named.

1. Why do taxonomists group by body plans first? _____

_____

_____

2. Why might taxonomists not include size and color among the criteria they

use for classifying? _____

_____

_____

3. Why do taxonomists use many criteria when classifying?_____

_____

_____

4. Why is scientific classification of organisms important? _____

_____

_____

Name _____

Compare Classification Systems

Work in pairs. Compare and contrast the two classification systems. Both systems use the same set of animals. Consider what you know about taxonomists and classification systems to answer the following questions.

System 1: Name the criteria used in each step.

1. Step 1 _____

2. Step 2 _____

3. Step 3 _____

System 2: Name the criteria used in each step.

4. Step 1 _____

5. Step 2 _____

6. Step 3 _____

An organism has already been classified using either System 1 or System 2. The organism is an egg-laying, land animal.

7. Circle the system that was used to classify it.

   System 1   System 2

8. What additional criteria were used to classify it?

   _____

   _____

9. Which animal(s) fits the criteria?

   _____

Name _____

Compare Classification Systems, continued

An organism has already been classified using either System 1 or System 2. The organism is a feathered vertebrate.

10. Which system was used to classify it?

   System 1   System 2

11. What additional criteria were used to classify it?

_____

12. Which animal(s) fits the criteria?

_____

13. Can you determine the purpose of these two classification systems? Why or why not?

_____

_____

_____

14. Can you determine what beliefs support the use of these systems? Why or why not?

_____

_____

_____

Name _____

Animals That Acquire Blood

Research the following organisms and complete the table.

Animal	Where does it live?	What is its prey?	How does it acquire blood?
mosquito	in trees	People/animals	fly's to its prey and grabs it
vampire bat	in caves	insects	fly's to it
tick	in grassy areas	human	falls on it when walking under
leech	in ponds like	every living thing	when its prey is swimming to it and grabs it
flea	on animals	animal	in jumps on it
lamprey	in lakes like	People/animals	it uses its funnel like mouth and sharp teeth to

Use the information to compare the organisms and complete the table.

How the organisms are similar	How the organisms are different
1. They acquire blood	1. They live in different places
2. They need blood to live	2. They have different prey
3. They all have sharp teeth	3. They use different ways to catch there prey.
4. There creatures.	4. There different creatures

Name _____

Metamorphosis

Research one animal that develops by metamorphosis.

1. Draw and label the animal in each stage of its metamorphosis.

2. Briefly describe the changes that occur in each stage of your animal's metamorphosis.

_____

_____

_____

_____

3. Why is metamorphosis considered a unique form of animal development?

_____

_____

_____

_____

Name _____

Match the Organism to the Habitat

Read the descriptions of each organism and consider its unique features. Draw a line from the organism to the habitat it is uniquely designed to survive in.

Organism	**Habitat**
1. Tapeworm: The eggs of tapeworms are eaten by animals. When digestion starts, the eggs respond by hatching and growing into larvae.	**A.** Mt. Makalu in Nepal is covered with glaciers so few organisms live there. Predators find very little to prey on.
2. Lichen: Lichen need very little water and can withstand extremely high temperatures. They are able to acquire nutrients from rocks and algae.	**B.** Most organisms need sunlight in order to survive, but sunlight seldom reaches into the deep inner sections of caves.
3. Jumping spider: These spiders can survive long periods of time without food while buried in the snow.	**C.** The intestines of an animal are warm and sheltered from many threats. To get into the intestines of an animal, an organism must be eaten.
4. Snottite: These bacteria do not need any exposure to sunlight because they are able to acquire enough energy from substances that contain sulfur.	**D.** California's Death Valley can go without rain for months, and temperatures on the surface of rocks can reach 66° C (150° F).

Determine the type of habitat the organism lives in. Explain your answer.

5. Naked Mole Rat: These rodents are virtually blind, have no external ears, and have massive front teeth in mouths specially designed for digging.

_____

_____

_____

Name _____

A New Habitat

1. What is your favorite animal?

_____

2. Describe the features of your favorite animal.

_____

_____

3. How do these features help the animal survive in its habitat?

_____

_____

4. Pick a new habitat that is very different and describe it.

_____

_____

5. Describe how you would re-design your favorite animal to survive in this new habitat. Explain why each new feature would be necessary. Consider the body plan and the five characteristics of living things as you re-design the animal.

_____

_____

_____

6. After your re-design, do you still have the same animal? Explain.

_____

_____

_____

_____

Name _____

Choose a Tool

Read each task. Choose two tools that will complete each task best and explain what method you used to complete it.

1. Task: Move sand from one bowl to another without touching the bowls.

Tool 1: _____

Method 1: _____

Tool 2: _____

Method 2: _____

2. Task: Move marbles from one bowl to another without touching the bowls.

Tool 1: _____

Method 1: _____

Tool 2: _____

Method 2: _____

Read each task. Choose one tool that will complete both tasks and explain what method you used to complete them.

3. Tool: _____
Task 1: Cut the bread into pieces and move it one piece at a time onto the paper towel without touching the bread with your hands.
Method 1: _____

Task 2: Move some of the sand into the water and stir without touching the bowls.
Method 2: _____

4. Fill in the blanks: Different tools can be used for the same _____ and

the same tool can be used for different _____.

© *Purposeful Design Science, Level Four* • Diversity of Life

Name _____

Paige and Daisy

Read the paragraph below and complete the exercises.

Six years ago Paige was in a car accident that left her paralyzed from the waist down. She also has limited use of her arms. Though in a wheelchair, Paige lives a very normal life thanks to her friend Daisy, a service dog. Paige's day begins with breakfast. Daisy uses her nose to flip on the lights and her paws and nose to open the refrigerator. Daisy carefully uses her mouth to pick up an egg and place it on the counter. Daisy uses her mouth to open a cupboard, take out a pan, and place it on the counter. Paige cooks breakfast. Later, the phone rings. Daisy runs and picks it up with her mouth and carries it to Paige. When it is time for Paige to go to the park, Daisy uses a leash and harness to pull Paige's wheelchair. Anytime that Paige needs help, Daisy runs and barks until someone comes. Thanks to Daisy, Paige can do almost anything!

1. Circle five instances in which Daisy uses part of her body to complete a task. Compare how Daisy performs the task and how Paige would have performed the same task before her accident. Complete the table.

Task	Comparison

2. On the previous page, you used two different tools to complete the same task. How does this relate to the comparison you made above?

_____

3. Which of the comparisons you made above are similar to using the same tool for different tasks?

_____

Name _____

Snake Tongues

Read the paragraph and examine the illustration. Use the information to complete the questions below.

As something gives off a smell, it sends microscopic particles into the air. A snake waves its tongue in the air to gather these particles. If the smell is coming from the left of the snake, the left fork of the snake's tongue picks up more particles than the right fork of its tongue. The snake then inserts the forks of its tongue into two tiny holes in the roof of its mouth. The holes are connected to a special structure called a Jacobson's organ. This organ tells the snake that the object is to its left.

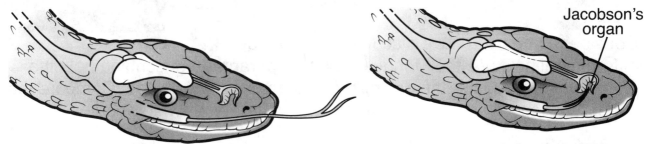

Jacobson's organ

1. Contrast the way a snake determines the location of distant objects to how a person determines the location of distant objects.

_____

_____

2. How is your answer to item one an example of the diversity found among living things?

_____

_____

3. Compare the functions of the human tongue to those of a snake's tongue.

_____

_____

Name _____

Okapi

Read the paragraph below.

Okapis are gentle creatures that live in the rain forests of central Africa. The front end of an okapi looks like a small giraffe and the back end looks like a zebra. Okapis have long black tongues that they use to grasp leaves that are higher than they can reach with their mouths. Okapi tongues are very long. An okapi is able to use its tongue to clean its eyes and even its ears!

Consider all that you have discovered about how different animals use their tongues. Write a paragraph describing how the okapi is an example of the diversity found among living things. Compare the okapi to at least two different animals that you have learned about.

_____

_____

_____

_____

_____

_____

_____

_____

_____

Name _____

What kind of fossil is it?

Read the paragraph below. Mark the kind of fossil you see in each picture.

There are four major kinds of fossils: trace fossils, mold fossils, cast fossils, and true fossils. Trace fossils, including footprints, are formed when an organism makes a mark, and that mark becomes a fossil. Mold fossils form when an organism dies and a dent is left in the shape of its body or part of its body. Cast fossils are formed when a material like mud fills in the dents of a mold fossil, making a replica of the body or body part. True fossils, like an animal frozen in a glacier, contain the actual organism or parts of the actual organism.

1.

○ **Trace**   ○ **Mold**

○ **Cast**   ○ **True**

2.

○ **Trace**   ○ **Mold**

○ **Cast**   ○ **True**

3.

○ **Trace**   ○ **Mold**

○ **Cast**   ○ **True**

© *Purposeful Design Science, Level Four • Diversity of Life*

Name _____

Assemble the Skeleton

When scientists find a group of fossilized bones, they try to put them together to form a complete skeleton. Usually, some of the bones are missing. To put the skeleton together, they use what they know and then make an educated guess about what the missing bones are like. They make the missing bones out of plaster, plastic, or concrete. The bones below represent fossils that scientists might find. Look carefully at their shapes and sizes to determine what kind of animal they came from. Then, in the large box, draw the skeleton. Also draw the missing bones to make the skeleton complete.

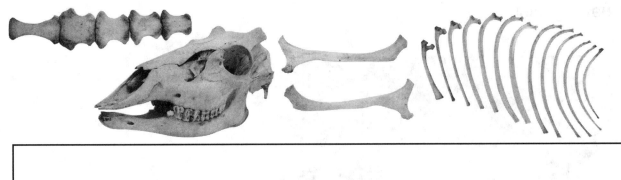

1. How did you know how to arrange the bones?

_____

_____

2. How did you determine what the missing bones looked like?

_____

_____

Name _____

Vocabulary Review

ACROSS

1 One of a kind

8 A developmental change in the form of an animal

10 To find the way from one place to another

DOWN

2 To navigate or locate objects by sending out and receiving sounds

3 A wide range of unique features in a group

4 An organism that lives in or on another organism, acquiring materials from it and harming it

5 Physical remains or an imprint of an organism that lived in the distant past

6 The development of an offspring inside its mother's body before being born

7 A chemical substance that is released by an organism for the purpose of communication and behavioral change

9 No longer existing

Name _____

Chapter 3 Review

Read the clues and give examples of how the following organisms are unique:

1. Frog (development): _____

2. Elephant (reproduction): _____

3. Vampire bat (acquiring materials): _____

4. Tapir (response): _____

5. Lamprey (acquiring materials): _____

Describe how each animal is an example of how this statement is true:
Organisms are uniquely designed to survive in their habitats.

6. Polar bear

_____

_____

7. Camel

_____

_____

8. A giraffe uses its tongue to grasp its food the way that humans use their hands. Describe how this is an example of diversity.

_____

_____

9. A scientist has just discovered a fossil of an animal's jaw. The jaw has six-inch long, sharp teeth. What steps would a scientist follow to understand and identify this animal?

_____

_____

_____

Name _____

Fix the Flashlight

Work as a group to put the flashlight together.
Answer the questions.

1. Consider the definition of a system and explain how it applies to
the flashlight.

Definition of a system	How does the definition apply to a flashlight?
A group of parts	
that work together	
to perform a task.	

2. How many parts does the flashlight have? _____

3. How do the parts work together?

_____

_____

4. What is the function of a flashlight?

_____

_____

5. Would the flashlight work if the bulb were burned out?_____If the battery

were dead?_____If the switch were missing?_____Why or why not?

_____

_____

6. Is the flashlight a system? Explain.

_____

_____

Name _____

Is it a system?

Use what you learned about the flashlight system to determine if each of these items is a system. Circle **Yes** or **No** and explain your answer.

7. Is a food chain a system?

Definition of a system	How does the definition apply to a food chains?
A group of parts	
that work together	
to perform a task.	

Yes   No   Explain your answer. _____

_____

_____

_____

8. Is a rock a system?

Definition of a system	How does the definition apply to a rock?
A group of parts	
that work together	
to perform a task.	

Yes   No   Explain your answer. _____

_____

_____

_____

4.1C
NOTEBOOK

Name _____

Is it a system? (continued)

9. Bob, Mary, Tommy, Suzy, and Grandma Joyce live together. The parents, Bob and Mary, have jobs in order to provide things like clothes and food. Tommy and Suzy do their homework and complete their chores. Grandma Joyce helps with the household and is always there to help Tommy and Suzy. They do these things in order to take care of each other. Is this a system?

Yes   No   Explain your answer. _____

_____

_____

_____

_____

10. Name a system _____

Definition of a system	How does the definition apply to this system?
A group of parts	
that work together	
to perform a task.	

Explain why it is a system. _____

_____

_____

_____

_____

_____

Name _____

Systems within Systems

Read the paragraph. Use the information to complete the page.

A cell is the basic building block of living things. The human body is made of various kinds of cells, such as nerve cells, blood cells, and muscle cells. Cells are made of parts such as a cell membrane, cytoplasm, nucleus, and organelles. Each of these parts works together so that the cell functions as the kind of cell it is. Groups of the same kinds of cells work together to make tissue. Nerves carry signals between body parts and the brain. Blood circulates to carry oxygen and nutrients to the body. Muscles contract to move the body. Nerve, blood, muscle, and other kinds of tissue work together so that the human body can perform the tasks necessary to survive and thrive. The human body is a system.

1. Is a tissue a system? Yes or No?

Definition of a system	How does the definition apply to a tissue?
A group of parts	
that work together	
to perform a task.	

2. Is a cell a system? Yes or No?

Definition of a system	How does the definition apply to a cell?
A group of parts	
that work together	
to perform a task.	

3. Explain how the human body provides examples of a system within a system.

_____

_____

_____

_____

Name _____

A Frog's Niche

Look at the frog and read the information. Complete the exercises below.

- *Eats insects*

- *Reproduces in water*

- *Is eaten by raccoons*

- *Hops or swims away from danger*

- *Is decomposed by bacteria after death*

1. What does a frog need to thrive?

_____

_____

2. How does this frog's niche meet the needs of other organisms?

_____

_____

3. Predict how each scenario would affect the frog:
A drought causes the pond water to decrease. _____

_____

_____

The fly population is reduced by pesticides. _____

_____

_____

Most of the raccoons are killed by hunters. _____

_____

_____

Name _____

Fill in the Web

Examine the organisms below. Draw arrows from each organism to another that is dependent on it. Write *producer*, *consumer*, or *decomposer* next to each organism. Answer the questions below.

1. Name examples of how two of the organisms in the illustration are dependent on one another and explain why.

   _____

   _____

2. Choose one organism that is a predator and one that is prey. Describe how each is designed to survive.
   Predator

   _____

   _____

   Prey

   _____

   _____

3. Propose a situation that would cause this habitat to be out of balance or cease functioning.

   _____

   _____

4. Determine what abiotic factors affect these organisms.

   _____

Name _____

Energy Flow

Look at the illustration and answer the questions.

1. What is the main source of energy on Earth?

_____

_____

_____

2. How are all organisms that are not producers dependent on producers?

_____

_____

_____

3. Give an example of a decomposer. Describe its role in an ecosystem.

_____

_____

_____

4. How does energy flow keep an ecosystem in balance?

_____

_____

_____

5. How does energy get from the sun into your steak?

_____

_____

_____

Name _____

Cycles

Draw the water and carbon cycles. Use the words below to label the parts.

precipitation	producers	consumers
decomposers	condensation (clouds)	ocean, lake, stream
carbon dioxide	evaporation	

Water Cycle

Why is the water cycle important?

_____

_____

_____

Carbon Cycle

Why is the carbon cycle important?

_____

_____

_____

Name _____

Minor or Severe Imbalance

Read each paragraph and answer the questions.

Southeast Asian Disaster

On December 26, 2004, a huge earthquake in the Indian Ocean caused a tsunami that damaged many islands and coastlines in Southeast Asia. Hundreds of thousands of people were killed. The tsunami also affected the marine ecosystems of many places, including the Bay of Bengal. Most of the coral reefs in this ecosystem were crushed. Sand built up in the reefs, choking them. Many of the species that depended on the reefs had to find a new habitat.

1. What caused the ecological changes? _____

2. How did this create imbalance in the ecosystem? _____

_____

3. Did the change cause minor or severe imbalance? Explain your answer.

_____

_____

Devastation in Northern Africa

In 2004, a huge swarm of locusts landed in southern Mauritania, a nation in northern Africa. Locusts can eat an amount of food equal to their body weight every day, so they devastated the crops and other plant life in the entire region. When the locusts left, almost no green plants had survived, and it was too late in the season for new plants to grow.

1. What caused the ecological changes? _____

2. How did this create imbalance in the ecosystem? _____

_____

3. Did the change cause minor or severe imbalance? Explain your answer.

_____

_____

Name _____

Pollution Conclusions

Based on your observations from the experiment, answer the questions below.

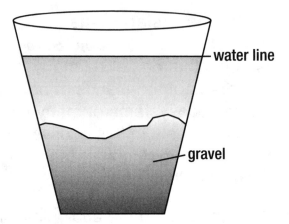

water line

gravel

1. If the cup with gravel and water represents a lake, what does the water that seeps into the gravel represent?

_____

_____

2. The food coloring represents pollution. When pollution is spilled into lake water, does it also affect the groundwater? Explain your answer. _____

_____

_____

3. If people who live near a polluted lake drink the groundwater, what might happen? _____

_____

4. To clean polluted lakes, people sometimes pump the water out of the lake, treat it, and put it back. Can they remove all the pollution in one try? How could they prevent pollution from happening? _____

_____

_____

_____

_____

Name _____

Understanding the Food Web

Organisms on this food web consume organisms listed below them. The lines on a food web represent the specific things organisms eat. For example, a line connects the lion to the gazelle. This means that lions eat gazelles. Another connects the gazelle to the leaves. This means that gazelles eat leaves.

In order to understand the relationships between the organisms on this food web, look at the lines and fill in the blanks below.

Hyenas consume:_____

Hyenas are consumed by: _____

Lions consume: _____

Lions are consumed by:_____

Jackals consume:_____

Jackals are consumed by:_____

Gazelles consume:_____

Gazelles are consumed by:_____

Grasses consume:_____

Grasses are consumed by:_____

Name _____

The Effects of Change in an Ecosystem

In the spaces below, describe each event. Then, based on classroom discussion, describe the possible long-term impact of each event.

1. Event:_____

Possible long-term impact:

_____

_____

2. Event:_____

Possible long-term impact:

_____

_____

3. Event:_____

Possible long-term impact:

_____

_____

4. Event:_____

Possible long-term impact:

_____

_____

5. Event:_____

Possible long-term impact:

_____

_____

Name _____

Restoration or Prevention

Read the following items and decide if each one is an example of restoration or prevention. Write **R** next to the ones that are examples of restoration and **P** next to the ones that are examples of prevention. If you think it may be both, write a **B**.

_____ **1.** The town dump is nearly full. The townspeople decide to start recycling so that they do not have to use more land to make the dump bigger.

_____ **2.** A factory near a forest preserve goes out of business. The city government decides to tear down the buildings, plant trees, and make the land part of the forest preserve.

_____ **3.** An oil spill has hurt a population of sea otters. Scientists volunteer to catch and clean the sea otters so that they can be released into the wild.

_____ **4.** A population of lions has dropped because of over-hunting. The government decides to make it illegal to kill lions.

_____ **5.** A family needs to buy a new car. They decide to spend a little extra money to buy a car that gives off less air pollution than others.

_____ **6.** A forest has been destroyed by logging. The people who live nearby decide to plant one tree for every tree that was cut down.

_____ **7.** Too many foxes are getting hit by cars on a country road. The town decides to lower the speed limit on the road so that drivers can avoid hitting the foxes.

Name _____

Oil Ordeal

Read the following paragraph. Use the information to complete the exercise.

On the night of March 23, 1989, a ship named Exxon Valdez was carrying millions of gallons of oil through Prince William Sound, a beautiful area in the Gulf of Alaska that is home to hundreds of species of birds, fish, and other animals. At approximately midnight the ship hit a reef that tore a hole in the ship's side. Oil spilled into the gulf. The wind and waves spread the oil over many miles, soiling beaches where sea birds, seals, and otters lived. Thousands of fish, birds, and other animals died because the oil poisoned them or prevented their fur and feathers from keeping them warm. The ecosystem was devastated. The company that operated the ship accepted responsibility for the spill and for the next four years worked with the United States Coast Guard, the U.S. Environmental Protection Agency, and many volunteers to remove the oil. Beaches were washed with water and detergent. Skimmers were used to remove oil from the water's surface. Specialists cleaned oil off otters, seals, birds, and other animals. Now the ecosystem is recovering. To prevent such a spill from happening again, the U.S. Congress passed laws that require higher standards in ship building and waterway control.

Explain how the *Exxon Valdez* oil spill ordeal included imbalance, restoration, and prevention. Use specific examples from the paragraph to support your explanation.

_____

_____

_____

_____

_____

_____

_____

Name _____

Vocabulary Review

Read the sentences and unscramble the words to fill in the blanks.

1. Zoos practice _____ _____ to

prevent endangered species, like the panda, from becoming extinct.

(VTPCAIE GDBEIENR)

2. Protecting and restoring species and resources is called

_____. (RVOITANESOCN)

3. An oxpecker eating insects off a zebra is an example of

_____. (ISOYSMIBS)

4. The living and nonliving things that surround an organism provide it with

the _____ it needs to survive. (CROSUEERS)

5. Cutting down too many trees results in

_____. (SDTEAFTOIROEN)

6. A tapeworm lives in the stomach of its _____. (OHTS)

7. Illegally killing an animal is called _____.

(CPHOIANG)

8. The introduction of a _____

_____ usually disrupts the _____

of the ecosystem and may endanger the _____

_____ that live there. (ONEFRIG SICEPES)

(CBLANEA) (VTEIAN SICEPES)

Name _____

Vocabulary Review, continued

9. Each organism is part of a habitat where its _____
are met. (SEDEN)

10. The release of harmful chemicals into our soil, air, or water is called
_____. (LTOINULOP)

11. A _____ _____ shows the feeding relationships
and the _____ for resources among
organisms in an ecosystem. (DOFO EBW) (TEPICITOMON)

12. Neither _____ nor
_____ is considered a _____
because they are not behaviors. (OEAGLFUACM) (YICIRMM)
(EFESDEN)

13. Each organism fills a role or _____ in its habitat. (HECIN)

14. _____ are transferred and circulated
through cycles. (UTTEISNRN)

15. Energy from the sun, in the form of sunlight, is transferred to organisms
by _____ _____.
(GEENRY WFOL)

16. Carbon and water are transferred through _____
_____. (LATANRU LECCYS)

Name _____

Chapter 4 Review

Name the three requirements of a system.

1. _____

2. _____

3. _____

An organism's needs are met by what two types of resources?

4. _____ 5. _____

6. Explain an example of competition in nature. _____

_____

_____

_____

_____

7. Explain an example of symbiosis. _____

_____

_____

_____

_____

8. Explain why all organisms in an ecosystem are dependent on

decomposers. _____

_____

_____

_____

_____

4.8D
NOTEBOOK

Name _____

Chapter 4 Review, *continued*

A factory spills oil into a river. Answer the questions below.

9. The oil spill is an example of what type of pollution?

_____   _____

(TWRAE LLOPTUION)

10. How will the oil spill affect the living things in and around the river?

_____

_____

_____

_____

_____

11. How can the oil spill be cleaned up? _____

_____

_____

_____

_____

12. What can be done to prevent the oil spill from happening again?

_____

_____

_____

_____

_____

Name _____

Energy Scavenger Hunt

In the spaces below, identify three living things that use energy and three nonliving things that use energy. Then describe where they get the energy they use, how they get the energy they use, and what they do with the energy they use.

Living Things

1. _____

_____

_____

2. _____

_____

_____

3. _____

_____

_____

Nonliving Things

4. _____

_____

_____

5. _____

_____

_____

6. _____

_____

Name _____

Purposeful Design Science, Level Four • Energy and Heat

Rubber Band Shoot

Materials needed: one small rubber band, one metric ruler, one metric tape measure

Using the ruler and rubber band, shoot the rubber band 15 times from the floor as shown in the diagram. Use the tape measure to find how many centimeters the rubber band has flown. Record this distance below.

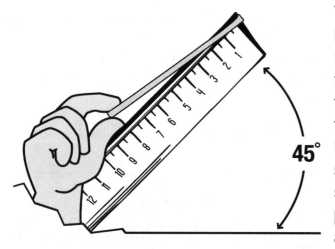

The first five times, shoot the rubber band by stretching it to the 8-cm mark and then releasing it. The next five times, pull the rubber band back to the 10-cm mark. The final five times, pull it back to the 12-cm mark. Make sure that for every shot, the shooting end of the ruler is at the shooting line. Also, be careful to point the ruler at a 45-degree angle above the floor each time.

Finally, clear the landing area so that your rubber band does not hit anything or anyone. When finished, find the average distance the rubber band flew for each group of five shots by adding the numbers for all five shots and dividing the sum by five. Round your answers to the nearest whole number.

Stretch length	8 cm		10 cm		12 cm	
Distance	Shot 1:	cm	Shot 1:	cm	Shot 1:	cm
	Shot 2:	cm	Shot 2:	cm	Shot 2:	cm
	Shot 3:	cm	Shot 3:	cm	Shot 3:	cm
	Shot 4:	cm	Shot 4:	cm	Shot 4:	cm
	Shot 5:	cm	Shot 5:	cm	Shot 5:	cm
Sum of all 5 distances						
Average (Sum divided by 5)						

Name _____

Conservation of Energy

The principle of the conservation of energy states that energy can change form, but cannot be created or destroyed. On the picture, label all of the different forms of energy you can identify.

Then, describe three examples of energy being transferred to other forms of energy.

1. _____

_____

_____

_____

_____

_____

2. _____

_____

_____

_____

_____

3. _____

_____

_____

_____

Name _____

Work and Force

1. Roll the car to your partner. Watch for increases and decreases in speed and changes in direction. Note any objects in the car's path that may have caused these changes in speed or direction. In the box below, draw yourself and your partner. Include a dotted line to indicate the path of the car. Label instances of work and any forces that affected the path of the car.

```




```

2. When you rolled the car, how was potential energy transferred to kinetic energy? _____

_____

_____

3. Roll the ball to your partner, but do so by bouncing it off of a wall or some other object. Again, watch for increases and decreases in speed, and changes in direction. Note any objects on the ground that may have caused these changes in speed or direction. In the box below, use a dotted line to draw the path of the ball from yourself to your partner. Label instances of work and any forces that affected the path of the ball.

```




```

4. When you rolled the ball, how was potential energy transferred to kinetic energy? _____

_____

_____

Name _____

How is thermal energy transferred?

Complete the steps and answer the questions below.

1. Hold a thermometer in one of the cups and add 100 milliliters (mL) of hot water. Read and record the temperature. _____

2. Consider the materials the cups are made of. Which cup of water will cool down the most in 30 minutes? Which will cool the second most, and which will cool the least? _____

_____

_____

3. Test your prediction with more hot water from your teacher.

  a. Fill the remaining cups with exactly 100 mL of hot water and write down the exact time. _____ (Example: 2:08) Place the lid over the paper cup. What time will it be when 30 minutes have passed? _____ (Example: 2:38)

  b. After 30 minutes have passed, measure and record the temperature of the water in each cup. (Allow the thermometer to cool for 30 seconds between cups.)

	Plastic	STYROFOAM®	Paper with Lid
Temperature			

4. How accurate was your prediction? In other words, compare what you predicted to what actually happened. _____

_____

_____

Name _____

How is thermal energy transferred? (continued)

5. Why did the water in the cups get cooler? In other words, how did the movement of particles in the cooler air surrounding the cups affect the movement of the water particles inside the cups?

_____

_____

_____

6. Why did the water in the different cups cool at different rates?

_____

_____

_____

7. Describe what happened to the thermal energy levels in the different cups as they cooled down.

_____

_____

_____

8. Pictures at the bottom of page 59 in your textbook show types of clothing.

Which type of clothing most resembles the STYROFOAM® cup? _____

Which type of clothing most resembles the plastic cup? _____

Which type of clothing most resembles the paper cup? _____

Which type of clothing most resembles the lid? _____

Explain your answers. _____

_____

_____

Name _____

Butter Melt

Follow the directions in the experiment below. Use your observations to answer the questions.

1. Use a plastic knife to cut two small pieces of butter and place one in the middle of the handle of each spoon—one metal, one plastic. See the illustration at the right for an example of how far down to place the butter. Wait for your teacher to give you hot water for your cup. Make sure that the butter will be just above the water without touching it. Do not yet place the spoons in the water.

2. Predict what you think will happen to the butter on each spoon when the spoon is placed in the hot water.

_____

3. Place both spoons, handle up, in the cup of hot water.

4. Using a clock or timer, observe the butter on each spoon and record what you see after…

30 seconds _____

1 minute _____

1 minute and 30 seconds _____

2 minutes_____

5. Which butter melted first? Explain why.

_____

_____

_____

_____

Name _____

Compare Scenarios

Read the two scenarios below. Use the information to answer the questions.

Ocean warming	Jack's car
Radiation from the sun reaches the water in the ocean. The water is warmer around the equator than in the rest of the ocean.	The windows in Jack's car have been open. Jack gets in the car and feels no change in temperature. The air in the car and the steering wheel are the same temperature as the air outside.

1. Which scenario has heat described in it and why?

_____

_____

_____

2. In the scenario that describes heat, explain the ways thermal energy is being transferred.

_____

_____

_____

3. Using the scenario that does not have heat, explain why thermal energy is not transferred.

_____

4. Differentiate between thermal energy and heat.

_____

_____

_____

Name _____

Egg Drop Challenge

Read the challenge in the box. Work with a partner to design a way to meet the challenge.

Materials needed: one raw egg, one STYROFOAM® cup, one meter stick, latex gloves, various padding materials, masking tape

> **Challenge:** Drop an egg from a height of 1 meter onto the floor without it breaking.

1. Use a STYROFOAM® cup and your choice of padding material to design a container that will keep the egg from breaking. Describe your container below.

   _____

   _____

2. Place your egg in your container. Use a meter stick to help you find the correct height. Drop your egg. Did you meet the challenge? Explain why or why not. If not, what could you do to improve your container's design?

   _____

   _____

   _____

3. a. Describe what kind of energy the egg had before, during, and after you dropped it.

   before: _____

   during: _____

   after: _____

   b. Explain how energy can be transferred out of a falling egg to prevent

   the egg from breaking. _____

   _____

   _____

Name _____

Rubber Band

Complete the activity at Station 1. Place an X in the boxes that name the kind of energy present at each stage of the stretching process. Circle the best word to describe the temperature of the rubber band before and after stretching.

BEFORE: cool   room-temperature   warm

AFTER: cool   room-temperature   warm

Station 1 Rubber Band

Stage of Stretching	Potential Energy	Kinetic Energy	Thermal Energy	Explain how energy is transferred at each stage
1. at rest (beginning)				
2. stretching				
3. stretched				
4. contracting				
5. at rest (end)				

Where did the thermal energy at the end come from?

_____

_____

_____

_____

_____

Name _____

Bouncing Ball

Complete the activity at Station 2. Place an X in the boxes that name the kind of energy present at each stage of the bouncing process.

Temperature before bouncing: _____ **Temperature after bouncing:** _____

Station 2 Bouncing Ball

Stage of Bouncing	Potential Energy	Kinetic Energy	Thermal Energy	Explain how energy is transferred at each stage
1. at rest (beginning)				
2. being thrown				
3. impact				
4. bouncing up				
5. at rest (end)				

Where did the thermal energy at the end come from? _____

_____

_____

_____

_____

_____

_____

Name _____

Compare Temperatures

Observe the three thermometers. Record their temperatures and answer the questions below.

1. Record the temperatures of the thermometers below.

#1 thermometer in water	
#2 thermometer in foil	
#3 thermometer in bubble wrap	

2. Rank the temperatures from highest to lowest.

Highest	
Middle	
Lowest	

3. Explain why the thermometers had different temperatures. _____

_____

_____

_____

_____

Name _____

Raw Materials

With the materials given to you, create a mechanism or tool of some sort. Make sure to use all of the materials. When you have finished, draw a picture of it in the space below. Label the materials that were used and answer the questions.

1. What purpose can your mechanism or tool be used for?

_____

_____

2. Describe how energy interacts with the materials in your mechanism or tool. How is it put into the mechanism or tool? How does it come out of the mechanism or tool? How is it stored in the mechanism or tool?

_____

_____

_____

_____

_____

_____

Name _____

Electroscope

Materials needed:
student-made electroscope   comb   metric ruler

Follow the instructions provided by your teacher. Construct an electroscope and answer the questions below.

1. Your electroscope is designed to exhibit two forms of kinetic energy. Predict what the forms of kinetic energy are.

_____

_____

2. Have one student comb his or her hair with the comb for 60 seconds. Bring the comb to within one centimeter of the copper wire. Make sure to touch nothing other than the comb, and make sure the comb does not touch the wire. Observe the aluminum foil and record your observations.

_____

_____

_____

3. Was your prediction correct? If not, describe the difference between what you predicted and what actually happened.

_____

_____

_____

4. How did the electroscope allow you to see matter and energy interacting in a way that the mechanism or tool you created did not?

_____

_____

_____

5.8A
NOTEBOOK

Name _____

Vocabulary Review

Write the number of the word on the blank of its definition.

1. heat   _____ energy associated with position or the arrangement of parts

2. kinetic energy   _____ energy associated with motion

3. thermal energy   _____ energy can change form, but it cannot be created or destroyed

4. convection   _____ the push or pull of one thing on another

5. potential energy   _____ a force applied to an object causing it to move

6. conduction   _____ energy associated with the random motion of particles in matter

7. insulator   _____ a measure of thermal energy in matter

8. work   _____ a measure of the amount of the thermal energy transferred between two objects having different temperatures

9. radiation   _____ the transfer of thermal energy through solids

10. force   _____ matter that promotes the transfer of thermal energy

11. conductor   _____ matter that slows down the transfer of thermal energy

12. conservation of energy   _____ the transfer of thermal energy through liquids or gases

13. temperature   _____ the transfer of energy by waves

© *Purposeful Design Science, Level Four* • Energy and Heat

Name _____

Chapter 5 Review

Examine the illustration below. Use the information to answer the questions.

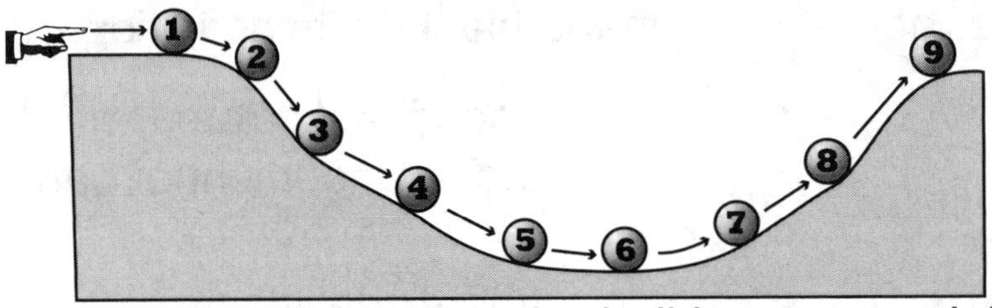

1. At which position or positions does the ball have potential energy?

_____ kinetic energy? _____

2. What forces make the ball move?

Position 1 to 2: _____

Position 2 to 5: _____

3. Is the movement of the ball considered work? Why or why not?

_____

_____

Examine the illustration. Use the
information to answer the questions.

4. How is thermal energy being transferred?

_____

_____

5. Explain the difference between thermal energy and heat.

_____

_____

6. If a pond freezes, is its thermal energy being destroyed? Why or why not?

_____

_____

Name _____

Waves

Sit approximately 4.5 meters (15 feet) from your partner. Hold one end of the metal spring toy while your partner holds the other end and rest the stretched spring on the ground. Follow the directions and answer the questions below.

While your partner holds his or her end of the spring in place, move your end back and forth on the ground. Adjust the motion of your hand until you are able to produce waves that look like those in Boxes 1, 2, and 3. Keep in mind that the wave pattern in each box is what you would see when looking down from above the spring toy.

Box 1

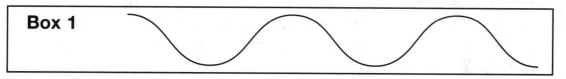

Describe the motion of your hand that resulted in waves like the ones in Box 1.

_____

_____

Box 2

Describe the motion of your hand that resulted in waves like the ones in Box 2.

_____

_____

Box 3

Describe the motion of your hand that resulted in waves like the ones in Box 3.

_____

_____

Name _____

Light and Sound

Thunder is the sound created by lightning. When you hear thunder, you are really hearing the lightning itself. Sometimes you do not hear the thunder until many seconds after you see the lightning. That is, you do not *hear* the lightning until many seconds after you *see* the lightning. Why is this? Did you know that the farther away lightning strikes, the longer it takes to hear it? The following activity will also illustrate this relationship between light and sound.

When you pop a balloon with your hand, you see it and hear it, the way you see and hear lightning. In this activity, your teacher will pop balloons at distances that are farther and farther away. Answer the question under *Predict*, below. Use your eyes and ears to observe the popping balloons and anything else that changes as your teacher walks farther and farther away. Write down your observations under *Observe*. These observations will help you answer the final question under *Explain*.

Predict

Will there be a gap between when you see and hear the balloons pop? Why

or why not? _____

_____

Observe

Was there a gap between when you saw the balloons pop and when you

heard them pop? _____

If so, at which distances were you able to notice a gap between when you

saw the balloons pop and heard them pop? _____

_____

Explain

Why do you think this happened? _____

_____

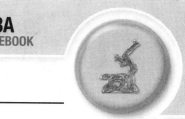

Name Gavin Andrews

Transverse and Longitudinal Waves

Follow the directions and write your observations.

1. Stand with a rope held loosely between you and your partner. Flick your wrists back and forth to produce transverse waves.

Did you make transverse waves? Explain. Yes because the movement of our wrist caused the rope to move at the same time

2. Stand with the rope stretched between you and your partner. Take turns trying to push and pull the rope to produce longitudinal waves.

Did you make longitudinal waves? Explain. Yes because it made only a single wave down.

3. Fill a small box two-thirds full of marbles. Quickly shift the box to the left and to the right to produce transverse waves.

Did you make transverse waves? Explain. Yes because when I moved the box Left and Right the marbles went up then tumbled over the rest

4. Now quickly push the box forward and pull it back to produce longitudinal waves.

Did you make longitudinal waves? Explain. Yes because when I pushed it forward the marbles went up and when I pulled it it went back and went up

© *Purposeful Design Science, Level Four* • Light and Sound

Name Gavin Andrews

Sound

Listen to the sounds that are made by the ruler and spoons. How are the sounds produced?

1. Ruler: when banged on the the table the ruler made a snaping sound.

2. Spoons: when banged on the table the spoons made a sound like a rock hiting metal.

Follow the directions and write your observations.

Phone: Make a small hole in the bottom of both paper cups. Thread one end of the string through the bottom of one cup and tie a knot inside the cup. Thread the string through the other cup and tie a knot inside the cup. Have your partner hold one cup to his or her ear while you hold the other to yours. Make sure that the string is tight. Whisper into your cup while your partner listens. Reverse roles and repeat the activity.

3. How did the cup and string affect the sound of your partner's whisper?

It tuned every thing out.

4. What material(s) did the sound travel through in the phone activity?

paper and horse hair.

Name _____

What makes up sunlight?

Answer the following questions:

1. Show the path of light from the sun to the prism to the paper.

Sun   **Prism**   **Paper**

2. List the colors of the visible spectrum,
in the correct order, on the diagram above.

3. Which color bent the most? _____

4. Which color bent the least? _____

5. Place a thermometer in the colors until the temperature stops changing.

Record the highest temperature reached. _____

6. Place the thermometer above the red region and not in any of the colors.

Record the highest temperature reached. _____

7. Place the thermometer below the violet region and not in any
of the colors.

Record the highest temperature reached. _____

8. Describe any differences in the temperatures measured.

_____

_____

Name _____

Putting the Spectrum in Order

The electromagnetic spectrum contains many types of EM radiation such as radio waves, visible light, gamma rays, ultraviolet rays, infrared waves, and x-rays.

Using the Electromagnetic Spectrum poster and your book, place each of these types of EM radiation in order from the longest to the shortest in the *Wavelength* column.

Do the same for the frequency and energy columns. Remember that if a wave has a long wavelength, it has a low frequency. Waves with high frequencies carry high amounts of energy.

	Wavelength	Frequency	Energy
Longest			
↕			
Shortest			

Which type of EM radiation has the lowest frequency? _____

Which type of EM radiation has the highest energy? _____

Which type of EM radiation has the shortest wavelength? _____

Name three ways in which x-rays are different from radio waves.

_____

_____

_____

Name _____

Trace the Reflection

Looking straight at the tracing pattern, place your green marker on *Start* and trace the line until you get to *Finish*. Next, look only at the reflection of the tracing pattern in the mirror. Place your red marker on *Start* and trace the line until you get to *Finish*. Answer the questions below.

1. Look at the accuracy of your green lines and red lines. Was it harder to trace the pattern while looking straight at it or while looking at its reflection? Explain your answer.

_____

_____

_____

2. As you traced the pattern while looking at its reflection, which was more difficult—tracing parts of the line that went to your left and right or tracing parts of the line that went toward and away from you? Explain your answer.

_____

_____

_____

_____

3. Now look at the reflection of your hand in the mirror. What happens as you move your hand toward the mirror?

_____

_____

_____

_____

Name _____

Stay in the Lines

Look only through the binoculars as you walk through the course. Your goal is to walk within the lines. Then, close one eye and look through the binoculars backward. Walk the course again as you look only through the binoculars. Answer the questions below.

1. Looking through the binoculars with both eyes, what did you see? How was this different than what you see without the binoculars?

_____

_____

_____

2. What was the most difficult thing about walking the course while looking through the binoculars with both eyes?

_____

_____

_____

3. Looking through the binoculars backward, with one eye, what did you see? How was this different than what you saw when looking with the binoculars forward and when looking without the binoculars?

_____

_____

_____

4. What was the most difficult thing about walking the course while looking through the binoculars backward with one eye?

_____

_____

Name _____

Make a Kazoo

Materials needed: wax-paper square, 6 cm (2.5 in.) cardboard tube, two rubber bands, and a sharp pencil

Wrap the wax-paper square over one end of the cardboard tube, like a lid, and secure it tightly with the rubber bands. You now have a kazoo.

Put the uncovered end of the kazoo up to your mouth and hum into it.

1. What happens to the covered end of the kazoo as you are humming into it?

_____

2. Now poke a small hole in the center of the wax paper with a sharp pencil and play the kazoo again. Describe anything that is different about the kazoo now.

_____

3. Describe what a kazoo sounds like.

_____

4. Make the hole in the wax paper bigger and play the kazoo again. Describe how this changed the kazoo.

_____

5. Ask a classmate to play a song together with you. How does producing music make you feel?

_____

6. Explain how a kazoo makes its unusual sound.

_____

_____

Name _____

Singing Glasses

Materials needed: four large glasses, water, spoon

Use the four glasses with different amounts of water in each to produce four different pitches by lightly striking them with a spoon. Adjust the amount of water in each until you have the right pitches to play the song *Mary Had a Little Lamb* or any other four-note song. Answer the following questions.

1. Complete the following drawing to show the amounts of water used to produce the four pitches.

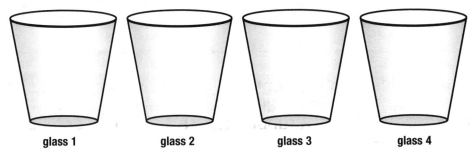

glass 1   glass 2   glass 3   glass 4

2. Label the drawing above showing which glass produced the highest pitch.

3. Label the drawing above showing which glass produced the lowest pitch.

4. Explain why these glasses produced different pitches.

_____

_____

5. Using the number under each glass, write in order which glass to hit to produce the song you played. For a pause, put an underscore (_). For instance, the song might start with 3212333_, etc.

_____

_____

_____

Name _____

Making a Spectroscope

Work in small groups. Follow the directions to build and use a spectroscope.

Directions

1. Draw a 2-cm wide by 4-cm high rectangle in the center of each end of the shoebox. Raise your hand and your teacher will use the utility knife to make a cut in each rectangle. Continue to cut out the rectangles with your scissors.
2. Cut one index card vertically in half. Tape the two halves of the index card over one of the holes. (Leave a vertical slit open that is about 0.5-cm wide.)
3. Cut a 2-cm wide by 4-cm high piece of diffraction grating and place it over the remaining rectangular hole in the box. Lightly tape the grating in place.
4. Put the top on the box. Put a rubber band around both ends of the box to hold the top in place.
5. Hold the shoebox so that the slit is facing a light source. Make sure that the slit is oriented vertically. (❙) Look through the diffraction grating. You should see colors. Congratulations, you've made a spectroscope!

If you do not see the spectrum extend to the left and the right, the scratches on the grating are not parallel to the slit. Remove the diffraction grating, rotate it 90 degrees, and try again. When the spectrum extends left and right from the slit, securely tape the grating in place.

Light Sources

Use your spectroscope to look at light from as many different light sources as possible, such as light bulbs, tungsten-halogen bulbs, fluorescent lights, vapor light, neon light, candlelight, and sunlight. (You can see the visible spectrum by looking at sunlight reflecting off a piece of white paper. Do not look directly at the sun!)

Name _____

Light Spectrum

Using your spectroscope, illustrate and label two spectra produced by different light sources. Describe how they are similar and how they are different. Complete the exercise.

Light #1	Light #2

Describe how the two types of light are similar.

_____

_____

Describe how the two types of light are different.

_____

_____

You may use your textbook as a resource.
1. What is the electromagnetic spectrum?

_____

2. What type of electromagnetic waves can be seen with your spectroscope?

_____

3. What type of invisible electromagnetic waves can be detected with a thermometer?

_____

4. List, in order, the colors in the visible spectrum.

_____

_____

Name _____

Vocabulary Review

Read the sentences and unscramble the words to fill in the blanks.

1. A way of transferring energy from one place to another without matter being transferred is called a _____. (AWVE)

2. Glass or plastic, shaped in order to focus light, is called a _____ _____. (OXCVNE NSLE)

3. The _____ _____ is the entire wavelength range of electromagnetic radiation. (ECNEETMLIGACORT UCRESPTM)

4. _____ _____ are waves in which the vibration is side to side or up and down. (EASETRNSVR EASWV)

5. All of the wavelengths of light that can be seen are within the _____ _____. (IVLSIEB REUPTMSC)

6. The _____ of a wave is the distance from one peak to another. (GVELAWTEHN)

7. The part of the electromagnetic spectrum that includes television and cell phones is the _____ _____. (DORIA EURTSMPC)

8. _____ is the height of a wave. (LUIDTAEPM)

9. The frequency of a sound wave is called its _____. (HCPTI)

10. If you are a sound wave, then the matter through which you travel is called your _____. (DMIMUE)

11. _____ _____ are waves in which the vibration is forward and backward. (IONGILANTDLU SEWVA)

Name _____

Chapter 6 Review

Circle the answer most closely associated with the phrase.

1. Moves very fast   *Light*   *Sound*

2. Does not need a medium   *Light*   *Sound*

3. Is not electromagnetic radiation   *Light*   *Sound*

4. Involves the audio spectrum   *Light*   *Sound*

5. Is similar to x-rays   *Light*   *Sound*

6. Is seen by the retina   *Light*   *Sound*

Fill in the blanks with the correct word.

7. A _____ is a communication that encodes information.

A _____ is a device that converts information into a signal.

A _____ is a device that receives a signal.

8. You just finished measuring the distance a wave traveled in one direction in a certain amount of time. What have you determined about the wave?

_____

9. You need a lens that will make objects look smaller by spreading light out. In the box, draw a picture of this lens including lines showing the path of several light rays.

What kind of lens
do you need?

_____ lens

Name _____

Observe Motion

Follow the directions below and then complete the chart using what you observe and what you know about motion. Under *Description of Motion,* describe the direction that the object moves. Under *Examples of Other Objects,* list at least two other items that move in a similar way to a ball, coin, or string and paper clip.

1. Sit on the floor across from your partner. Roll, throw, and bounce a tennis ball back and forth to each other. Observe the ball's movement.

2. Spin your coin and observe its movement.

3. Tie a paper clip at the end of a string. Swing the string back and forth. Swing the string slowly in a circle. Observe the paper clip's movement.

	Description of Motion	**Examples of Other Objects**
ball		
coin		
string and paper clip		

Name _____

Describe Motion

Use what you have observed and what you know to answer the questions and complete the activities below.

1. What causes a tennis ball and coin to move straight? What causes them to spin?

_____

_____

2. What causes a paper clip to swing? What changes the direction of its motion?

_____

_____

3. What causes a moving object to stop?

_____

_____

4. Place a note card on top of a cup. Place a coin on the card. Quickly pull the card out from under the coin. What happens to the coin?

_____

_____

5. Explain why you think the coin on the note card does not move the same way the note card does.

_____

_____

_____

_____

Name _____

Force Experiment

Experiment with contact and noncontact forces. Complete the exercises below.

1. Stand facing your partner. Put the palms of your hands together and lean toward one another. What force does your partner exert on you?

_____

2. Have your partner sit down and hold out his or her hands. Joining your hands together, try pulling your partner across the floor. What force makes it difficult to pull someone across a surface?

_____

3. With your partner, pull on a rope until it is taut (tight). Identify which kind of force the rope has when it is taut.

_____

4. Throw a paper airplane. What force slows the plane and what other force brings it to the ground?

_____

5. Quickly rub two sheets of paper together for ten seconds. Lay them on top of each other on a desktop so that one end hangs over the edge of the desk. Grab a corner of the top sheet and lift it quickly. Describe what happens and identify the force involved.

_____

_____

6. Crumple one sheet of paper. Take the crumpled paper and a sheet of flat paper and hold them out. Drop them both. Describe what happens and explain what forces are involved.

_____

_____

_____

7.3B
NOTEBOOK

Name _____

Chart the Forces

Use the experiments from the previous page to fill in the chart below. Identify the forces involved in each experiment and determine if they are contact or noncontact. List other examples of each type of force. (Do not use examples from your textbook.)

Activity	Forces involved	Contact or noncontact	Example
pushing against a partner			
pulling a partner			
pulling a rope with a partner			
throwing an airplane			
rubbing two sheets of paper together			
throwing a crumpled sheet and a flat sheet of paper			

Name _____

Jar Roll

Watch your teacher's demonstration and complete the steps below.

1. Examine the jar filled with sand and the jar filled with packing peanuts. Which one is heavier?

_____

2. Which jar do you think will roll farther? Explain your answer.

_____

_____

3. Place the jar filled with sand at the top of the 3-ring binder. Position it so that when it is released, it will roll straight forward from the binder. Release it without pushing it. Using the measuring tape, measure how far it rolls. Write the distance in the table below. Repeat twice and record the distances below.

4. Follow the same procedure with the jar filled with packing peanuts. Write the distances of all three rolls in the table below.

	Sand	Packing Peanuts
Roll #1		
Roll #2		
Roll #3		

5. Calculate the average length of the rolls for the jar filled with sand by adding the three rolls and dividing the sum by three. Round to the nearest whole number. The average length the sand-filled jar rolled is _____. Do the same for the jar with the packing peanuts. The average length the packing peanut-filled jar rolled is _____. Which jar rolled farther on average? _____

6. Using Newton's First Law, explain why one jar rolled farther than the other.

_____

_____

Name _____

Ball Drop

Complete the exercises below.

1. Stand still directly above the target. Hold a ball waist high and drop it on the target. Repeat two more times. Were you able to hit the target? _____ If so, how many times? _____ If not, did you come within a few centimeters of hitting the target? _____

2. As the picture below illustrates, place your feet behind the starting line and run toward the finish line as fast as you can. As you pass the target, try to drop the ball on it. Repeat three times. Were you able to hit the target? _____ If so, how many times? _____ How do these results compare with those from the previous exercise?

_____

_____

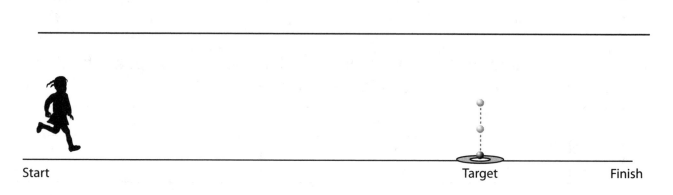

Start   Target   Finish

3. Explain why it was easier to hit the target or come close to it while you were standing still than when you were running. Make sure to mention where you released the ball when you were running toward the target. Explain your results in terms of Newton's First Law.

_____

_____

_____

_____

_____

Name _____

Newton's Second Law of Motion

Complete the activities and exercises below.

1. Push the empty cardboard box, the box filled with books, and the box filled with pillows from *Start* to *Finish*. Compare your three pushes and describe them in terms of Newton's Second Law of Motion.

_____

_____

_____

2. Explain why the boxes stop moving when you stop applying force.

_____

_____

_____

3. Use pencils or pens to make the boxes easier to push across the floor. Describe how you did it and why it worked.

_____

_____

_____

_____

4. Imagine that you are playing with a little brother or neighbor child. You are pulling the child in a wagon. When you get tired and sit down in the wagon, the child tries to pull you. He soon discovers that he cannot move the wagon nearly as fast as you can. Explain why he cannot.

_____

_____

_____

_____

Name _____

Newton's Third Law of Motion

Follow the directions below to complete the experiment. Answer the questions.

1. Secure the lid on one film canister and place it on the floor on its side.

2. Fill the second canister half-full with water. Place half of an effervescent tablet in the water and secure the lid on the canister. Quickly place this canister on the floor next to the first canister so that the lids face each other.

3. Stand back and watch what happens. Record your observations.

_____

_____

_____

_____

_____

_____

4. Use Newton's Third Law of Motion to explain what happened to the canisters.

_____

_____

_____

_____

_____

_____

Name _____

Athletic Motion

Examine the images displayed. Identify the types of motion you see and describe them. Identify them as *translation*, *rotation*, or *vibration*. Some pictures have more than one type of motion represented.

Number	Describe the motion you see.	What kind(s) of motion is(are) represented?
1		
2		
3		
4		
5		
6		

© *Purposeful Design Science, Level Four* • Motion and Force

Name _____

Apply Newton's Laws

Consider the scenarios below. Apply Newton's laws to each scenario to explain the motion.

You are riding on a bus on the edge of your seat. Each time the bus speeds up, you fall backward against your seat. Each time the bus slows down, you bend forward.

Describe the motion.

_____
_____
_____
_____
_____

Your friend gets a new pellet gun for Christmas. He decides to shoot it at a metal target. The pellet bounces back at him and shatters a glass jar nearby.

Describe the motion.

_____
_____
_____
_____
_____

Two baseball pitchers are competing to see who can throw farther. Both can throw with the same speed, but one throws a baseball and the other throws a sponge ball.

Describe the motion.

_____
_____
_____
_____
_____

Name _____

Move the Books

Use only rubber bands to move both books across the table. Complete the exercises.

1. Set one book at the end of the desk. Place the cut rubber band on this book so that about half of the rubber band hangs over the edge of the book. Place the second book on top of the first book, trapping the rubber band between the two books.

2. Pull on the rubber band and try to force the books to slide across the desk. Describe what happens.

_____

_____

3. Discuss with your group a plan to modify your method so that you can successfully pull the books across the desk. Explain your plan here.

_____

_____

4. Try out your plan. Describe what happens.

_____

_____

5. Using the terms *force*, *friction*, and *inertia*, explain why your method worked or did not work.

_____

_____

_____

_____

_____

Name _____

Does money have inertia?

Use the coins to conduct the activities below. Complete the exercises.

1. Place a stack of five coins on your desk. Create sides around the edge of your desk by using books or other materials. Using the index card, quickly knock the bottom coin out of the stack without touching the other coins above it. Continue knocking out the bottom coin until no coins remain in the stack.

2. Explain why this activity works.

_____

_____

3. Design a method to knock two coins out at once. Describe your method.

_____

_____

4. Repeat the first exercise, pushing slowly on the bottom coin with the index card. Explain what happens this time and why.

_____

_____

5. Hold your hand palm up with just your index finger extended. Now place a coin on the index card and balance it on your finger. Quickly pull the card out from between your finger and the coin. Repeat until the coin remains balanced on your finger after the card is pulled away. Explain why this activity works.

_____

_____

_____

Relative Motion: Ball Bounce

Follow the directions to complete the experiment. Complete the charts and answer Number 3.

1. Find a location from which you can see the balls bouncing. Observe carefully as your teacher drops the balls. Each time the balls are dropped, determine which one hits the floor first. After each drop, put an **X** in the appropriate box on the data table. For all five drops, observe from the exact same location and position.

	Red Ball	*Green Ball*	*Tie*
Drop 1			
Drop 2			
Drop 3			
Drop 4			
Drop 5			

2. Move to a new location according to your teacher's directions and watch again as the balls are dropped. Record your data in the table below.

	Red Ball	*Green Ball*	*Tie*
Drop 1			
Drop 2			
Drop 3			
Drop 4			
Drop 5			

3. Consider the different answers of your classmates. Explain why all the responses are not the same for every person.

_____

_____

_____

_____

Name _____

Apparent Motion: Flip Book

Directions:
   a) Your teacher will give you the supplies needed for this activity.
   b) Distribute the drawings of the legless bugs to each member in your group. Some students may have more drawings than others.
   c) Draw simple legs on each bug, attaching them to the bug's body at the small black dots.
   d) Once everyone in your group has finished, stack the drawings together neatly, and staple the papers in the top two corners.
   e) Let each student flip through the pages of the book several times and observe. Be sure to flip the pages slowly and quickly.

1. Describe what happens when you quickly flip through the pages of the flip book, and explain why this happens.

_____

_____

_____

2. What would happen if you took the pages of the flip book, pulled them apart, and stapled them back together completely out of their original order?

_____

_____

_____

_____

3. Name two other places where you can see apparent motion that is equivalent to the apparent motion of the bug in the flip book. Explain how each works.

_____

_____

_____

_____

Name _____

Vocabulary Review

Fill in the blanks with the correct vocabulary words.

1. A push or pull of one object on another through direct contact is called

_____ _____.

2. A movie is an example of _____ _____.

3. A force that resists stretching and squeezing is called

_____ _____.

4. A kite string resists stretching, creating _____.

5. An object's location or place is called its _____.

6. Motion described from a particular reference point is

_____ _____.

7. A change in an object's position is called _____.

8. _____ _____ is the force from an object

that pushes back against a contact force.

9. The space surrounding an object in which a noncontact force is active is

called a _____.

10. _____ is the motion of an object along some

path from one position to another.

11. _____ _____ is a push or pull

on an object without direct contact.

12. A motionless place or object used for comparison is called a

_____ _____.

13. _____ is back-and-forth or up-and-down motion.

14. The resistance to a change in motion is called _____.

Name _____

Chapter 7 Review

Name the three basic types of motion.

1. _____

2. _____

3. _____

Identify five types of force and note if they are contact or noncontact.

4. _____

5. _____

6. _____

7. _____

8. _____

Match Newton's Three Laws of Motion to their descriptions.

_____ 9. Newton's First Law

_____ 10. Newton's Second Law

_____ 11. Newton's Third Law

a. An object's ability to speed up is affected by its mass and the amount of force exerted on it.

b. Objects keep doing what they are doing unless they are acted on by unbalanced outside forces.

c. For every action, there is an equal and opposite reaction.

Circle the correct word to complete the sentences.

12. (Relative, Apparent) motion is the appearance of motion.

13. (Relative, Apparent) motion depends on a particular reference point.

Name _____

Compare Matter

Weigh the items at each of the first three stations. Describe their color, texture, and volume or size. Fill in the charts below and answer the question.

Station 1

	oil	water
weight		
color		
texture		
volume		

Station 2

	modeling clay	cornstarch and water
weight		
color		
texture		

Station 3

	wooden blocks	foam blocks
weight		
color		
texture		
size		

Consider the weights of the foam and wooden blocks. Why are their weights different even though they are the same size?

_____

_____

_____

Name _____

Compare Matter, continued

Follow the directions for Station 4. Answer the questions below.

Station 4

Part 1: Place both cans of soda in the water. Describe what happens to each

one. _____

_____

Part 2: Stretch the rubber and the cardboard.

Part 3: Squeeze the paper into a ball. Squeeze the aluminum foil into a ball.

1. Why does one soda can float and the other sinks?

_____

_____

2. Why are tires made of rubber and not cardboard?

_____

_____

3. Why does foil make a tighter ball than paper?

_____

_____

4. What makes one kind of matter different from another?

_____

_____

_____

_____

Name _____

Combine the Blocks

Use the building blocks your teacher gave you to build structures for each exercise. Draw the structures and answer the questions.

1. Build five identical structures using only three blocks in each structure. Draw one of these structures in the box below.

2. Arrange and connect the structures in the first exercise to form a larger structure. For example, arrange them so that there is the least amount of air between them or so that the structure is as stable as possible. Draw this arrangement in the box below.

3. How does the arrangement of the blocks affect the stability, shape, and size of the structure you made?

_____

_____

4. Think of another way to arrange your blocks to create a new structure. How is this structure different from the other?

_____

_____

_____

Name _____

Use the Table

Use the *Periodic Table of Elements* in your textbook to complete the exercises below.

1. Draw an oxygen atom in the space below. Give the chemical symbol for oxygen, the number of protons the oxygen atom has, and the chemical formula for an oxygen molecule.

2. Table salt has the chemical formula NaCl. Draw the atoms that make up salt. Write their names below them. Make sure your drawing includes the correct number of protons for each atom.

3. Describe what makes one kind of matter different from another.

_____

_____

_____

_____

Name _____

Sink or Float

Read through the activity below. Predict what you think will happen. Describe your observations and explain the result.

1. Measure 120 mL (1/2 cup) of water into a clear plastic cup. Add three drops of food coloring and stir.

2. Measure 120 mL (1/2 cup) of corn syrup.

3. Predict what will happen when you add the corn syrup to the water.

_____

_____

4. Add the corn syrup to the water. Describe what you see happening.

_____

_____

5. Now add the paper pieces to the water. Describe what happens to them.

_____

_____

6. Explain why one kind of matter floats in water while the other sinks.

_____

_____

_____

_____

Name _____

What properties does it have?

Follow the steps and answer the questions below.

1. Choose any object in your classroom and write its name: _____

2. On the lines below, list as many properties of the object as you can think of.

_____   _____

_____   _____

_____   _____

_____   _____

3. Now categorize the properties you listed as physical or chemical.

Physical	Chemical

4. What is the difference between physical and chemical properties and why is it harder to list chemical properties?

_____

_____

_____

_____

Name _____

Making Goo

Follow the directions below to observe a chemical reaction. Answer the questions.

1. Put on a pair of disposable gloves. Measure 15 mL (1 tbsp) of borax and 120 mL (1/2 cup) of warm water. What state of matter are these two substances? Describe their properties.

_____

_____

_____

2. In a bowl, mix the borax with the warm water. Describe the properties of this solution. Is this a physical or chemical change? Explain.

_____

_____

3. Measure 120 mL (1/2 cup) each of glue and water. Describe the properties of these substances.

_____

_____

4. In a bowl, mix the glue and water together. Describe the properties of this solution. Is this a physical or chemical change? Explain.

_____

_____

5. Using a separate bowl, pour the glue solution into the borax solution and stir.

6. A semisolid should form. Remove it from the remaining water solution and knead it to help it stick together. Use a paper towel to dry your hands, but do not touch the goo with the paper towel because it will stick. What vocabulary term(s) could you use to describe what has taken place? Why?

_____

_____

Name _____

Chemical Reaction Results

Using the information from the previous activity, fill in the descriptions below.

1. Identify the three reactants used in the experiment.

_____   _____   _____

2. Identify the product of the experiment.

_____

3. Describe the properties of this new matter. How is it similar to the reactants? How is it different from them?

_____

_____

_____

4. What is the difference between a physical change and a chemical change? Identify the physical and/or chemical changes that took place in the experiment.

_____

_____

_____

_____

_____

_____

Name _____

Atomic Model

Work in pairs to make a model of a nitrogen atom.

1. Use a compass to draw an 8-cm (3-in.) diameter circle on a sheet of white paper. This represents the nitrogen atom.

2. Use the compass to draw a 2-cm (1/2-in.) diameter circle on the red construction paper. This represents the nucleus.

3. Cut out the red circle and glue it in the center of the circle on the white paper.

4. Look at the element nitrogen (N) on the periodic table and determine how many protons and electrons it has.

5. Use the hole punch and punch out enough blue dots and yellow dots to represent the protons and electrons. Let the blue dots represent the protons and the yellow dots represent the electrons.

6. Glue the blue dots in the center of the nucleus.

7. Use the hole punch and punch out seven green dots to represent the neutrons. Glue the green dots in the nucleus with the protons.

8. Use the pencil to draw seven electron pathways. They should not connect with the nucleus. (Refer to the Bohr model in your textbook.)

9. Glue a yellow dot to each of the electron pathways. Place the electrons so they are less likely to smash into each other.

10. Label each part of your model and include your name on it.

Name _____

Why is it made of that?

Read the paragraph below. Determine what properties make the substance suitable for how it is used in computers.

Silicon is an element that is hard, dark gray, and shiny. Silicon is a semiconductor. A semiconductor is a material that conducts electricity. It does this better than an insulator like rubber but not as well as a conductor like copper. Copper is an element that is shiny, hard, and a very good conductor of electricity. Pure silicon conducts electricity very poorly. However, by adding other elements or by adjusting the electric field, silicon can become a very good conductor. These changes enable silicon to be the main substance used to make computer chips.

1. List the properties of silicon.

_____

_____

2. What is a semiconductor?

_____

_____

3. What is the main difference between silicon and copper?

_____

_____

4. What changes to silicon make it useful in computer chips?

_____

_____

Name _____

Identify the Change

Observe the substances at each station. Describe what you see and identify the change as physical or chemical.

Station 1: Dry Ice

Describe the change. Is it physical or chemical?

_____

_____

Station 2: Baking soda and vinegar

Describe the change. Is it physical or chemical?

_____

_____

Station 3: Effervescent tablet and water

Describe the change. Is it physical or chemical?

_____

_____

Station 4: Ice Cubes

Describe the change. Is it physical or chemical?

_____

_____

Station 5: Match

Describe the change. Is it physical or chemical?

_____

_____

8.6D
NOTEBOOK

Name _____

How do different kinds of matter interact?

Follow the directions for these two experiments. Describe how different kinds of matter interact.

1. Place several raisins in a cup of tap water. Describe what you see.

_____

_____

2. Place several raisins in a cup of soda water. Wait one to two minutes and then describe what you see.

_____

_____

3. Why do raisins react differently with soda water than they do with tap water?

_____

_____

4. Dip a corner of a paper towel in tap water. Use the wet paper towel to scrub one of the coins. Describe what happens to the coin.

_____

_____

5. Dip a corner of a paper towel in lemon juice. Use the juice to scrub one of the coins. Describe what happens to the coin.

_____

_____

6. Why does lemon juice react differently with the coin than tap water?

_____

_____

Name _____

Why this matter?

Consider the images below. Determine what materials they are composed of and why those materials were chosen for their construction.

_____
_____
_____
_____

_____
_____
_____

_____
_____
_____

_____
_____
_____

Name _____

Choices and Technology

Read the paragraphs below. Compare them and answer the questions below.

Blake just got a new computer for his birthday. He has to write a report about the country of Thailand for school. He uses the Internet to get information that will help him to understand the culture and geography of Thailand. Blake finds several articles on the Internet with a lot of information. He makes sure to use his own words when he writes his reports. He also includes the names of the authors whose articles he used as his sources. Blake learns a lot about Thailand and receives a good grade from his teacher.	Daniel just got a new computer for his birthday. He has to write a report on France for school. Daniel finds a website where he can download reports that were written by someone else. He copies a report, puts his name on it, and hands it in as if it were his own. Daniel's teacher, Mr. Smith, reads the report and is very disappointed. Mr. Smith can tell that Daniel copied the report instead of writing it himself. Daniel gets a failing grade on his report and gets sent to the principal's office for cheating.

1. What technology is being used in each paragraph?

_____

2. What is the difference between the way Blake uses technology and the way Daniel uses it?

_____

_____

3. What determines whether or not technology is good or bad?

_____

_____

_____

Name _____

Vocabulary Review

Use each of the following words correctly in a sentence.

1. density

_____

_____

2. chemical reaction

_____

_____

3. element

_____

_____

4. compound

_____

_____

5. model

_____

_____

6. chemical formula

_____

_____

7. technology

_____

_____

8. molecule

_____

_____

Name _____

Chapter 8 Review

Complete the following exercises.

Label each part of this atom. Use the periodic table to find out what element it represents.

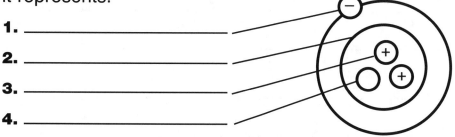

1. _____

2. _____

3. _____

4. _____

5. What element does this illustration represent? What is its chemical symbol?

_____

Read the information in the paragraph and answer Numbers 6 and 7.

Anita and her friends are building a campfire. Anita's father chops up pieces of wood and makes a pile. Anita lights the fire and watches it burn the wood. She and the other girls roast marshmallows. The marshmallows catch on fire and turn black on the outside. Anita breaks up pieces of chocolate and graham crackers. The girls put the marshmallows and chocolate on the crackers and enjoy a sticky treat!

6. Identify two physical changes and two chemical reactions in the paragraph.

_____

7. What is the difference between a physical change and a chemical reaction?

_____

8. Give an example of technology. Describe one way it can be used appropriately and one way it can be used inappropriately.

_____

_____

Name _____

What is under your bed?

Read the paragraph below. Fill in the box with labeled pictures of all the things that you might find under your bed.

When was the last time you looked under your bed? If your bed were suddenly turned into a drilling machine and could dig straight through the floor and into the earth, what would you find?

Under the bed, on or above the floor

Under the floor, on or above the ground

Under the ground

At the center of the earth

Name _____

Soil

Use your observations of the jar of *Soil* and the jar of
Soil and Sand to answer the questions below.

1. Do you notice any layers in the jars?
   If so, describe them. If not, explain why there are no layers.

   Soil jar: _____

   Soil and Sand jar: _____

   _____

2. Are some layers thicker than others? Why might this be?

   Soil jar: _____

   Soil and Sand jar: _____

   _____

   _____

3. Are all the particles in the soil the same size? What makes some smaller
   or larger than others?

   Soil jar: _____

   Soil and Sand jar: _____

   _____

4. Name some things that are in soil besides rock pieces and dirt. Explain
   why soil is important.

   _____

   _____

   _____

Name _____

Moving Plates

Use the materials to make a model of a convergent, divergent, and transform boundary. Reuse the same crackers and pudding for all three models. Before starting *Models 2* and *3*, pick up the crackers, redistribute the pudding, and reposition the crackers as indicated. Follow the steps to complete the activity and answer the questions.

Model 1

1. Place the crackers on the pudding, slightly apart as shown. Place your fingers on the outer edges of the crackers and gently push the crackers together.

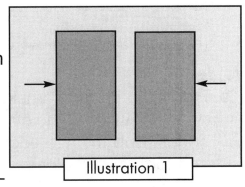

2. What happens when the crackers are pushed together?

_____

_____

3. What kind of boundary does *Illustration 1* represent?

_____

_____

_____

Model 2

4. Place the two graham crackers side by side on top of the pudding as shown.

5. Slowly and gently press the inside edges of the crackers down. Now pull them slightly apart as the picture at right illustrates.

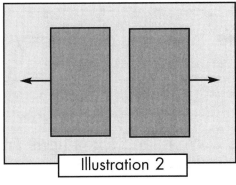

6. Describe what happened to the pudding when you pulled the crackers apart.

_____

_____

Name _____

Moving Plates, continued

7. What does the pudding represent?

_____

_____

8. What kind of boundary does *Illustration 2* represent?

_____

_____

Model 3

9. Place two graham crackers on the pudding. Line up the straightest long edges. Rub the two edges together back and forth as the picture at right illustrates.

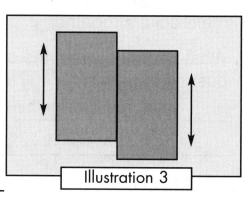

Illustration 3

10. What happens to the edges?

_____

_____

11. What do the graham crackers represent?

_____

_____

12. What kind of boundary does *Illustration 3* model?

_____

_____

13. What land formations and/or destructive activity occur along each of the three boundaries?

_____

_____

_____

Name _____

A Hike to the Waterfall

Follow the path with your finger. Label any area *P* where you see physical weathering, and *C* where you see chemical weathering.

Name _____

Physical Change

Observe the bottles. Then, try to relate them to things that might happen in the weathering of landforms on the earth's surface. Complete Numbers 1 and 2 and then answer the questions.

1. Draw the bottles before they are put in the freezer.

2. Draw the bottles after they have been frozen.

3. What happened to each bottle? _____

_____

_____

4. Why did this happen? _____

_____

_____

5. What might this represent, if it were to happen in nature? _____

_____

_____

6. How is it an example of physical weathering? _____

_____

_____

Name _____

Which layer?

Label the following objects according to the layer of soil in which they would be found. Write *T* for Topsoil, *S* for Subsoil or *B* for Bedrock. Some objects may have more than one correct answer.

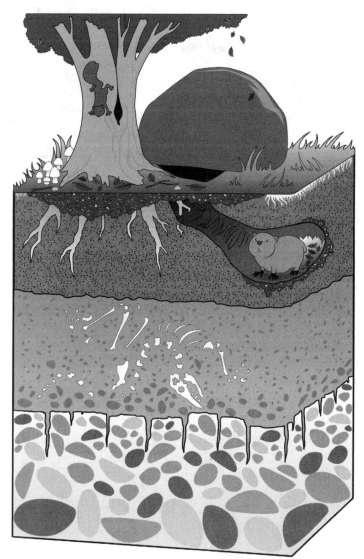

_____ **1.** large boulders

_____ **2.** a mouse

_____ **3.** tree roots

_____ **4.** humus

_____ **5.** flowers

_____ **6.** fossils

_____ **7.** fist-sized rocks

_____ **8.** grass roots

_____ **9.** a snake's hole

_____ **10.** grayish color

_____ **11.** light brown color

_____ **12.** dark brown color

Name _____

How does it fall?

Look at the illustrations below. Observe the particle size of each sample.
Then decide in what order they would deposit and form layers. Number
each one according to which layer you think it would be from top to bottom.
Use 1 to indicate the top layer and 5 to indicate the bottom layer.

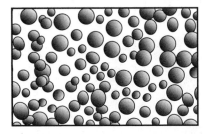

_____
(clay soil)

_____
(sand)

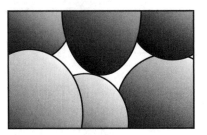

_____
*(large, close-fitting
boulders)*

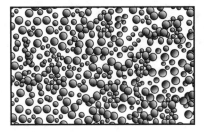

_____
*(dark-colored dirt with
some decayed matter)*

_____
*(pebbles and
small stones)*

Now draw a sample of what you think the layers would look like as
they deposited.

Name _____

Plate Tectonics

Read the information and steps below before beginning the activity. Your teacher will provide the materials. Follow each step carefully.

The earth's crust is always moving. When two plates rub against each other they cause movement and shaking of the ground.

Steps:
1. Lay newspaper on the table. Place the open sides of the two shoe boxes together, on top of the newspaper.
2. Line the shoe boxes with one piece of foil. Cover the foil with moist dirt, adding twigs, etc.
3. Use the plastic objects to build a neighborhood on top of the dirt and twigs.
4. With one hand on each end of the boxes, gently slide them against each other in opposite directions.
5. Observe what happens. Answer the questions below.

Analyze and Conclude:
1. Describe what happened when you rubbed the two boxes against each

other. _____

_____

_____

_____

2. Explain how this is similar to a transform boundary. _____

_____

_____

_____

3. What event can occur as a result of this type of movement? _____

_____

_____

_____

Name _____

Convection Currents in the Mantle

Read through the information and steps below before beginning the activity. Follow each step carefully.

Convection currents occur within the earth's mantle. As the magma heats up, it rises toward the top of the mantle. The cooler magma sinks toward the inner core. This creates convection currents which keep the mantle constantly flowing. In this experiment, you will model and observe how temperature and density changes cause convection currents.

Steps:
1. Fill the container half full of very cold water.
2. Measure one cup of very hot water and add 2-3 drops of food coloring.
3. Very slowly pour the hot, colored water into the cold water, pouring near the inside edge of the container. Observe.
4. Empty the container. Fill it half full of hot water.
5. Measure one cup of cold water and add 2-3 drops of food coloring.
6. Very slowly pour cold, colored water into the hot water. Observe.

Analyze and Conclude:
1. What happened to the colored, hot water when you added it to the cold

   water? _____

   _____

2. What happened to the colored, cold water when you added it to the hot

   water? _____

3. Which always sinks to the bottom—hot or cold water? _____

   _____

4. Based on this experiment, how does temperature affect convection in the

   mantle? _____

   _____

   _____

   _____

Name _____

Deforestation in the Amazon

The chart below shows the amounts of deforestation that occurred in the Brazilian Amazon between the years 1990 and 2005. Use the information on the chart to provide answers below.

Year	Deforestation sq. km	Deforestation sq. mi
1990	13,800	5,300
1991	11,100	4,200
1992	13,700	5,300
1993	15,400	5,900
1994	14,800	5,700
1995	29,000	11,000
1996	18,100	7,000
1997	13,000	5,000
1998	16,800	6,500
1999	17,200	6,600
2000	19,800	7,600
2001	18,100	7,000
2002	25,500	9,800
2003	24,100	9,300
2004	26,100	10,100
2005	18,900	7,300

1. What year experienced the greatest loss in forests?

_____

2. In what year did the least amount of deforestation occur?

_____

3. Between what years was there the largest increase in deforestation?

_____

4. Estimate the total square kilometers and/or square miles of deforestation that has taken place since 2000. Remember to round to the nearest thousand.

_____

Name _____

Deforestation: An In-Depth Look

Read the following paragraph that describes some of the basic practices of deforestation. Then, answer the questions below.

There are three basic types of deforestation: slash and burn agriculture, shade agriculture, and selective or clear cutting. Slash and burn agriculture is sometimes used when farmers need to plant crops or find a place for cattle to graze because they have no more nutrient-rich soil to use. They clear an area of several acres by cutting down all of the vegetation. Then they burn the cut trees to release the nutrients into the soil. Within a few years, the nutrients in the soil are washed away or used up. Shade agriculture is perhaps the least damaging type of deforestation. Farmers who grow shade-loving crops (like coffee and cacao) are able to leave many of the native trees intact. They grow their crops underneath the already existing shade trees. Selective cutting is a method loggers use when they cut some of the trees in an area and leave some uncut. Clear cutting, also used by loggers, is a method in which all of the trees in an area are cut down at once.

1. What are the basic types of deforestation?

_____

2. How is deforestation harmful to the living organisms (both plants and animals) in that area?

_____

_____

3. Do you think selective cutting or clear cutting is more damaging to the environment? Why?

_____

_____

4. Are there any advantages of deforestation?

_____

Name _____

Four Principles of Earth Science

In the boxes below draw a picture that represents each of the four principles of Earth Science. On the lines provided, describe how your drawing represents change or balance.

Lithosphere (the rocky layer that contains the crust and upper mantle)	Hydrosphere (Earth's waters)

_____   _____

_____   _____

_____   _____

Atmosphere (a mixture of gases surrounding the earth)	Universe (everything that exists)

_____   _____

_____   _____

_____   _____

Name _____

A Stranger's Journal

Read the information below and write a story that describes how the earth, water, the atmosphere, and the universe act as a system.

Imagine that you are a stranger from another galaxy. You have observed Earth's position in the universe from far off in space. You have come to Earth to discover how and why it has so many different forms of life on it. Write a journal about how all of the different parts of the earth work together to stay in balance and support life. Include the sun, water, atmosphere, and the needs of living things in your story.

Name _____

Vocabulary Review

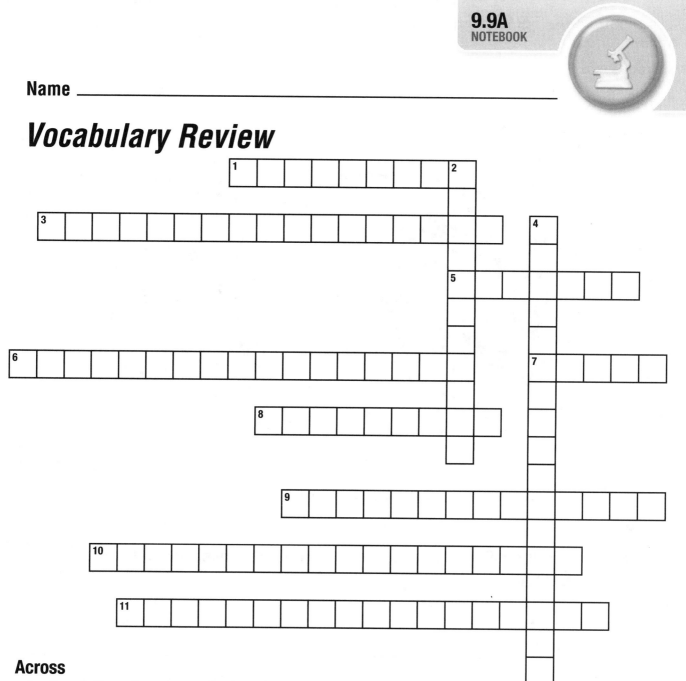

Across

1 Consisting of compounds that do not contain carbon

3 Plates that pull apart in opposite directions

5 Consisting of compounds that contain carbon

6 The circular movement of heated materials to a cooler area

7 A crack in the earth's plates along which movement occurs

8 A chemical change in which oxygen combines with another substance

9 The study of how the earth's lithospheric plates interact

10 The breakdown of rocks as a result of chemical reactions causing new substances to be formed

11 Plates that push together

Down

2 Process by which carbon dioxide dissolves in water

4 Plates that slide past each other

Name _____

Chapter 9 Review

Examine the illustrations below. Label the layers in the blanks below each diagram.

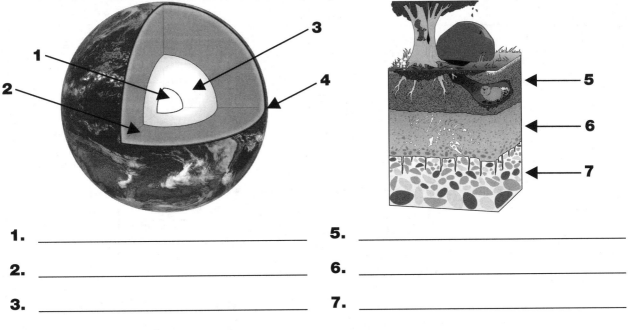

1. _____   5. _____

2. _____   6. _____

3. _____   7. _____

4. _____

8. Describe the difference between chemical and physical weathering and give an example of each.

_____

_____

9. In what two layers of the earth do convection currents occur?

_____

10. Explain how and why convection currents occur.

_____

_____

List the three types of plate boundaries that exist at the edges of the plates.

11. _____   13. _____

12. _____

Name _____

Water Is Everywhere

Many things on Earth are made of or contain water. Complete the word problems below to find out how much water is in each item being described.

1. About 9/10 of a watermelon is water. Color in the part of the watermelon that is water.

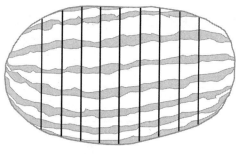

How much does 1/10 of a 20-pound

watermelon weigh? _____

How many pounds of water are in a 20-pound watermelon? _____

2. 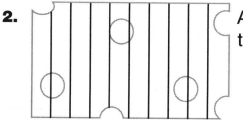 About 3/10 of cheese is water. Color in the part of the cheese that is water.

How much does 1/10 of a 5-pound block of cheese weigh? _____

How many pounds of water are in a 5-pound block of cheese? _____

3. About 2/3 of the human body is water.

How much does 1/3 of a 90-pound person weigh? _____

How many pounds of water are in that 90-pound person? _____

4. About 7/10 of a baby elephant is water.

How much does 1/10 of a 120-pound baby elephant weigh? _____

How many pounds of water are in a 120-pound baby elephant? _____

© Purposeful Design Science, Level Four • The Hydrosphere

Name _____

Where is the water?

Complete the following exercises to find out how important water is in your school.

1. Look around your classroom and observe all the items that contain water or the places where water might be used. List them below.

_____   _____   _____

_____   _____   _____

_____   _____   _____

2. Look around your school. List all of the items that contain water or ways that water is used.

_____   _____   _____

_____   _____   _____

_____   _____   _____

3. Choose three items from your lists that you consider the most important. Write them below and explain why they are important.

a. _____

_____

_____

b. _____

_____

_____

c. _____

_____

Name _____

Where does the water go?

Follow the directions below. Complete the observation exercises and answer the questions.

1. Using a marker, write your name on your piece of aluminum foil.

2. Put the piece of aluminum foil flat in front of you. Bend up the edges to make a small, shallow open-top box.

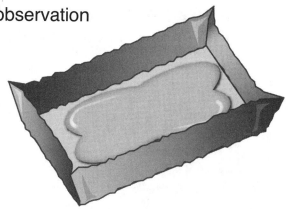

3. Pour just enough water into your box to barely cover the bottom.

4. Write down the time. Describe your box. Predict what will happen if the box is left in sunlight for half an hour.

    Time: _____

    Box: _____

5. Record how long the box was left in the sun.

_____

6. Describe what happened to the water in your box while the box was in the sunlight.

_____

_____

7. What part of the water cycle does this experiment demonstrate? What is the source of energy that keeps the cycle going?

_____

_____

_____

_____

Name _____

Identification of Water Stages

Look at the pictures below. Identify at least two parts of the water cycle that affect the objects in the pictures. Describe them in the blanks provided.

_____

_____

_____

_____

_____

_____

_____

_____

_____

_____

_____

_____

_____

_____

_____

Name _____

Compare Aquifers

Follow the steps to complete the experiment below. Answer any questions.

1. Place the Rain cup and the water aside.
2. Measure 60 mL (1/4 cup) of gravel into both the Soil and Soil and Sand cups.
3. Measure 60 mL (1/4 cup) of sand into the Soil and Sand cup.
4. Measure 120 mL (1/2 cup) of soil into both the Soil and Soil and Sand cups.
5. Put three drops of red food coloring onto the soil in both cups.
6. One group member should pick up the Soil cup and hold it up over a clean cup with no holes. Another group member should hold the Rain cup over the top of the Soil cup. A third group member should pour about half of the water into the Rain cup. Hold still until the water has drained out of the Rain cup and into the Soil cup. Set the Rain cup and water aside. Keep the Soil cup held up over the cup with no holes.

1. Wait two minutes and observe the water that drains from the *Soil* cup. Describe the water below.

_____

_____

2. Repeat Step 6 using the *Soil and Sand* cup. Wait two minutes and observe the water. Describe the water below.

_____

_____

3. What does the gravel represent in this experiment? Compare your descriptions above. Was there a difference between the two, and if so, why?

_____

_____

_____

Name _____

Namib Desert

Read the paragraph below. Follow the directions and write a paragraph describing your conclusion.

In most parts of Africa, groundwater that is used for drinking must first be boiled or filtered. This is because dirt and many different kinds of bacteria live in the ground. Water that is pumped out of the ground also contains dirt and bacteria. Sometimes these things can make people sick if they drink water. Filtering the water keeps some of the dirt and harmful bacteria from being consumed by people. Boiling the water kills the bacteria that might have contaminated it. In the desert nation of Namibia however, people can drink water straight out of the faucet.

Using your observations from the experiment on the previous page, determine why Namibians can drink their water without filtering or boiling it. Write a paragraph below describing your conclusion and how different kinds of soil affect groundwater.

_____

_____

_____

_____

_____

_____

_____

_____

_____

_____

_____

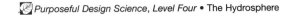

Name _____

Current Observation

Follow the directions to complete the experiment below. Answer the questions.

1. Pour the milk into the aluminum pan, filling the pan half full. Wait a few moments for the surface of the milk to become still.

2. Pretend that the pan is a clock. Put two drops of red food coloring on the surface of the milk right next to the edge of the pan where the number 12 would be on a clock. Where the number 3 would be on a clock, put two drops of yellow food coloring. Where the number 6 would be on a clock, put two drops of green food coloring. Where the number 9 would be on a clock, put two drops of blue food coloring.

3. Place one drop of liquid detergent into the center of the pan. Be careful not to disturb the milk.

4. Wait two minutes.
Draw what the colors look like in the empty circle at right.

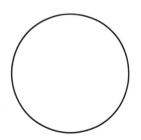

5. After two minutes, <u>gently</u> blow on the surface of the milk along one edge of the pan. Draw what you observe.

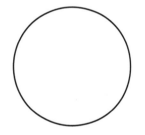

6. <u>Gently</u> blow on the surface of the milk along the opposite edge of the pan. Draw what you observe.

Name _____

Current Observation, continued

7. Gently blow directly into the center of the pan. Draw what you observe.

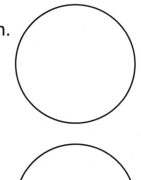

8. Gently blow across the surface of the milk. Draw what you observe.

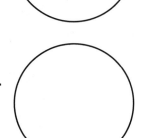

9. Place your hands on the sides of the pan. Very gently shake it. Draw what you observe.

10. How does the direction of the wind affect the ocean's currents?

_____

_____

11. What does shaking the pan represent? How does it affect the currents?

_____

_____

_____

_____

_____

_____

Name _____

Salinity Taste

Taste the water in each of the five cups by using a clean, dry cotton swab for each cup. Rank the taste from least salty to saltiest. Determine which one best represents each of the bodies of water described below.

1. Taste the water in each cup. Number the cups from least salty (#1) to saltiest (#5).

A   B   C   D   E

___   ___   ___   ___   ___

2. Using your ranking above, determine which cup best represents the bodies of water described below. Place the letter of the cup on the blank next to its description.

_____This sample represents the largest saltwater lake in the United States. It is called the Great Salt Lake and has a salinity of 172.

_____This sample represents the Red Sea, the body of water the Israelites passed through on their way out of Egypt. It has a salinity of 40.

_____This sample represents ocean water. It has a salinity of 35.

_____This sample represents the Dead Sea, which is the saltiest body of water in the world. It has a salinity of 293.

_____This sample was distilled water, which has been processed to rid it of all salt. It has a salinity of 0.

Name _____

Water Availability

Examine the bottle of water at the front of the classroom. On the bottle below, draw a line to show how much water is in the bottle. After your teacher has removed some water, draw a line to show the new level of water in the bottle.

Name _____

My Family's Water Usage

Use the chart you filled out to complete the calculations and determine your family's average daily water usage.

Two-Day Record	Calculate Average	Water Used per Day
1. wash dishes _____ + _____ = _____ _{Day 1 amount Day 2 amount Total A}	_____ ÷ 2 = _____ _{Total A Total B}	_____ x 113 liters = _____ _{Total B Total C}
2. flush toilet _____ + _____ = _____ _{Day 1 amount Day 2 amount Total A}	_____ ÷ 2 = _____ _{Total A Total B}	_____ x 19 liters = _____ _{Total B Total C}
3. take a bath or shower _____ + _____ = _____ _{Day 1 amount Day 2 amount Total A}	_____ ÷ 2 = _____ _{Total A Total B}	_____ x 100 liters = _____ _{Total B Total C}
4. brush teeth _____ + _____ = _____ _{Day 1 amount Day 2 amount Total A}	_____ ÷ 2 = _____ _{Total A Total B}	_____ x 19 liters = _____ _{Total B Total C}
5. wash clothes _____ + _____ = _____ _{Day 1 amount Day 2 amount Total A}	_____ ÷ 2 = _____ _{Total A Total B}	_____ x 200 liters = _____ _{Total B Total C}

6. Add all the *Total C*s together and write the total: _____ liters. This is an average number of liters of water your family uses every day!

Name _____

Avoid Wasting Water

For each of the following categories, describe a way that your family can reduce the amount of water used each day. Answer the question at the bottom of the page.

Wash dishes

_____

_____

Flush toilet

_____

_____

Take a bath or shower

_____

_____

Brush teeth

_____

_____

Wash clothes

_____

_____

Why is it important not to waste water?

_____

_____

_____

Name _____

Watershed

Follow the steps to complete the experiment below. Answer any questions.

1. Crumple your piece of paper into a tight ball. Open it back up and smooth it out. Do not flatten the paper completely.

2. Take a watercolor marking pen and mark all the crevices or wrinkles you see on the paper. You may use different colors.

3. Place your paper into the tin pan. Hold your cup with holes in the bottom over the top of your paper. Pour water into the cup with holes in it. Describe what you see.

_____

_____

_____

_____

4. What do the crevices or wrinkles on the paper represent?

_____

_____

5. Explain how this experiment demonstrates the way in which pollution might affect a watershed?

_____

_____

_____

_____

_____

Name _____

The Town of Glad

Read the story below. Write two endings to the story according to the directions below.

Once upon a time there was a little town called Glad. Glad had many little streams that all flowed into a main river called the Glad River. Almost all the citizens of Glad had a stream near their homes. The mayor of Glad, Mayor Don, had a stream that flowed right underneath his front porch. Every summer the people of Glad spent time splashing in their streams and boating on the Glad River. There were so many fish in the Glad River that it was easy to catch one. One day, a factory was built at the far northern end of town. Many of the people of Glad welcomed the factory because it produced Sky-High Balls. Sky-High Balls were made of rubber and bounced high in the air. They were fun to play with. After a while, the people began to notice a change. Their streams were turning gray. The Glad River began to stink, and no one could find a fish in it anymore. One day, Mayor Don looked down at the stream that flowed under his front porch and was horrified to find waste from the factory floating in it. Mayor Don called a town meeting and told the citizens of Glad that he had discovered the source of the pollution in Glad. It was the Sky-High Ball Factory. Mayor Don asked the citizens of Glad to vote on what should be done.

1. Write an ending to the story that reflects what you think will happen to Glad if its citizens choose to ignore the pollution.

_____

_____

_____

2. Write an ending to the story that reflects what you think will happen to Glad if its citizens choose to clean up the pollution.

_____

_____

_____

_____

Name _____

Vocabulary Review

Write the number of the word on the blank next to its definition.

1. artesian well   _____ a form of water that falls from the atmosphere to the earth

2. groundwater   _____ to mix with another substance to form a solution

3. transpiration   _____ the place where a river meets an ocean or sea

4. solvent   _____ groundwater trapped between layers of rock that flows to the surface through an opening

5. precipitation   _____ the change of a liquid to a gas

6. watershed   _____ the evaporation of excess water from a plant

7. evaporation   _____ water within the earth

8. dissolve   _____ a substance capable of dissolving another substance

9. salinity   _____ the amount of salt that is dissolved in water

10. estuary   _____ an area of land from which water drains into a particular water system

Name _____

Chapter 10 Review

Complete the exercises below to review the concepts in Chapter 10.

1. Draw and label a water cycle in the space below. Use the words in the box to correctly label it.

> evaporation
> precipitation
> condensation
> transpiration
> aquifer
> surface water
> groundwater
> estuary
> brackish

2. Describe a watershed. How does pollution dumped into a river affect a watershed?

_____

_____

3. Draw a molecule of water. Describe at least two properties that make water unique.

_____

_____

4. Which way do ocean currents flow in the Northern and Southern Hemispheres? How do ocean currents affect our weather?

_____

_____

_____

_____

_____

Name _____

Where will it go?

Your teacher has set up an experiment for you to observe.

1. Predict which direction you think the smoke will flow after the match is blown out. Explain why.

_____

_____

2. In the space below, draw the container of ice, hot plate, and match exactly how they were arranged. Then draw your observations of what happened to the smoke when the match was blown out.

3. In which direction did the smoke flow?

_____

_____

4. Why did it flow in this direction?

_____

_____

5. Compare your prediction to your observation.

_____

_____

Name _____

Making Predictions

Make several predictions based on your experience and observations. Then draw conclusions about the accuracy of predictions.

1. Obtain materials from your teacher. You will be placing drops of water on various coins with a small dropper. Use the data chart below to record your predictions and results.
2. Predict how many drops of water the penny will hold. Record your prediction.
3. Drop water on the penny until it is full. Count the number of drops and record.
4. Dry off the penny and repeat Step 3 two more times. Record the results.
5. Average the three trials and record.
6. Repeat the investigation using a nickel, dime, and quarter.

Coin Type	Prediction	1st Trial	2nd Trial	3rd Trial	Average
Penny					
Nickel					
Dime					
Quarter					

1. How accurate was your prediction for the penny?

_____

_____

2. Did your ability to predict improve for the other coins as you performed the activity? Why?

_____

_____

3. What have you concluded about making predictions?

_____

_____

Name _____

The Atmosphere

1. The atmosphere is a mixture of gases held close to Earth by gravity.

The mixture contains mostly _____, which

makes up _____ percent. _____, the

life sustaining gas, makes up _____ percent. The remaining

_____ percent is made of _____,

_____, and tiny particles.

2. Draw and label a circle graph to represent the gases in the atmosphere.

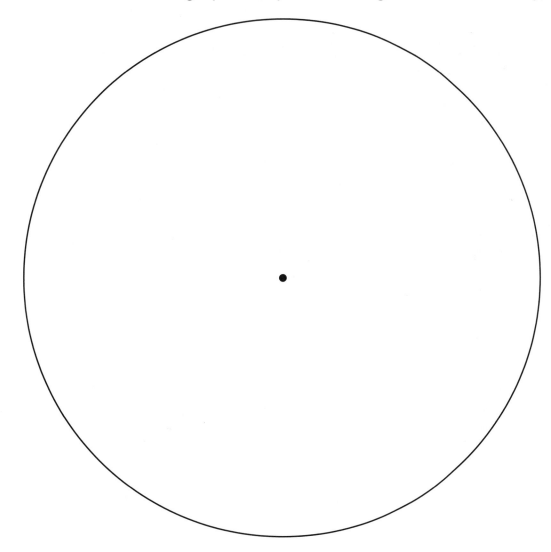

Name _____

The Atmosphere, continued

3. Match the layers of the atmosphere with their descriptions.

_____ troposphere   **a.** meteoroids burn in this layer

_____ stratosphere   **b.** begins at 550 km, extends towards outer space

_____ mesosphere   **c.** contains the ozone layer

_____ thermosphere   **d.** clouds and weather occur here

_____ exosphere   **e.** uppermost layer

4. Draw an illustration representing the layers of the atmosphere. Include the altitude of each layer.

Name _____

How does radiation affect the air?

Perform the following activity at home.

1. When you get up in the morning, stand by a window through which direct sunlight is shining. Then stand in the middle of the same room. Which place is warmer? Explain.

_____

_____

_____

_____

2. When you get home from school, stand at the same window and then in the middle of the room. Which place is warmer? Explain.

_____

_____

_____

_____

3. Walk around the house and find a room with direct sunlight coming in the window. Stand by the window and then in the middle of the room. Which place was warmer? Explain.

_____

_____

_____

4. Compare this room with the room you previously stood in. Was there any difference in temperature? Explain.

_____

_____

_____

Name _____

How does radiation affect the air? (continued)

Perform the following activity at school.

1. Get two thermometers from your teacher. Record the temperature on each one.

1ˢᵗ thermometer _____   2ⁿᵈ thermometer _____

2. Put one thermometer in a plastic bag. Lay a small piece of paper inside the bag on top of the bulb of the thermometer. Seal the bag. Place both thermometers on a sunny window sill. Lay a piece of paper on top of the bulb of the second thermometer. Predict what you think will happen.

_____

_____

3. Wait ten minutes. Check and record the temperature on each thermometer.

1ˢᵗ thermometer _____   2ⁿᵈ thermometer _____

4. Did the beginning temperatures change after putting the thermometers in the window? Why?

_____

_____

_____

_____

5. Was there a difference between the two temperatures on the window sill? Why?

_____

_____

_____

_____

Name _____

Fluffy Puffy Clouds

On a separate piece of paper draw a cumulonimbus, a cirrus, and an altostratus cloud.

Identify the names of four clouds in the coordinate puzzle below. The first number of each set is the horizontal coordinate. The second number is the vertical coordinate. For example, set (3,5) is L.

	1	2	3	4	5	6	7	8	9
9	R	U	M	T	U	R	D	L	B
8	O	A	U	R	U	B	S	U	A
7	S	K	U	S	M	U	I	H	A
6	C	V	U	E	C	T	N	F	S
5	F	D	L	M	N	O	P	T	U
4	R	Y	M	A	L	I	D	U	T
3	U	N	Q	R	P	S	A	S	T
2	E	L	G	T	J	F	T	C	L
1	I	T	A	C	S	O	A	V	T

1. ___ ___ ___ ___ ___ ___
(4,1) (6,4) (1,9) (4,3) (8,8) (6,3)

2. ___ ___ ___ ___ ___ ___ ___
(9,6) (6,6) (1,4) (9,8) (8,5) (6,7) (8,3)

3. ___ ___ ___ ___
(4,4) (8,9) (4,9) (1,8)

___ ___ ___ ___ ___ ___ ___
(1,6) (8,4) (3,4) (5,8) (9,2) (3,8) (1,7)

4. ___ ___ ___ ___ ___ ___
(5,6) (3,7) (5,7) (3,6) (5,4) (6,5)

___ ___ ___ ___ ___ ___
(5,5) (7,7) (4,5) (6,8) (5,9) (4,7)

© Purposeful Design Science, Level Four • The Atmosphere

Name _____

Rain, Rain, Go Away

Write a *T* if the statement is true. Write an *F* if the statement is false.

1. _____ Clouds are made of condensed water vapor.

2. _____ Hail is frozen rain larger than 5 mm in diameter.

3. _____ To describe a cloud higher than normal, the term *nimbus* is used.

4. _____ Cumulus clouds are found high in altitude.

5. _____ Snow forms when water vapor is directly converted to ice crystals.

6. _____ Sleet is another term for snow.

7. _____ Dew forms when water condenses on warmer surfaces.

8. _____ Humidity is the amount of water in the air.

9. _____ Most clouds have round bottoms.

Rewrite each false statement to make it true.

_____

_____

_____

_____

_____

_____

_____

_____

_____

Name _____

Convection Currents in the Troposphere

Fill in the blanks with the correct terms.

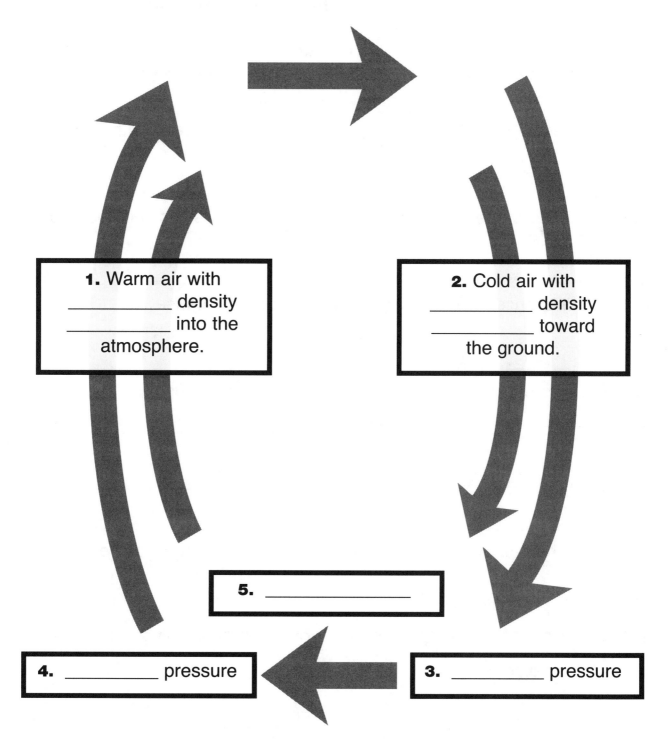

1. Warm air with _____ density _____ into the atmosphere.

2. Cold air with _____ density _____ toward the ground.

5. _____

4. _____ pressure

3. _____ pressure

Name _____

A Sign of Weather

Use the word bank below to complete the following statements.

clear	cloudy	dry	hurricane	gentle	barometer
rain	storms	strong	thunderstorms	tornadoes	

1. Low pressure foretells _____ skies and possible

_____ .

2. High pressure foretells _____ skies and possible

_____ weather.

3. Small differences between high and low pressures cause

_____ winds.

4. Large differences between high and low pressures cause

_____ winds and _____ .

5. Storms that produce lightning are called _____ .

6. A very strong spinning storm over a tropical ocean may become a

_____ .

7. Strong storms over land can produce thin, quickly spinning, low pressure

columns called _____ .

8. Meteorologists use a _____ to observe changes in

atmospheric pressure.

Name _____

Building a Barometer

Predict how a barometer will detect changes in air pressure. _____

_____

_____

Experiment

1. Obtain all the materials needed for this experiment from your teacher.

2. Stretch out the balloon several times. Blow it up until it is full, then let the air out.

3. Cut off the neck of the balloon. Stretch the balloon over the open end of the can so it lays flat across the top. Secure the balloon to the can with a rubber band.

4. Place a straw on top of the balloon. Arrange it so that one end of the straw extends 5 cm (2 in.) over the edge of the can. Tape the opposite end of the straw at the middle of the balloon.

5. In the middle of a piece of paper, using a ruler, draw a red line 10 cm (4 in.) long. Draw 5 blue lines above and 5 blue lines below the red line and make sure each line is at 2 mm intervals. Mark the lines above with a + and the lines below with a −.

6. Place the can on a table next to the wall (away from the sun) with the straw pointing toward the wall.

7. Hold the paper against the wall so the free end of the straw is pointed at the red line. Tape the paper to the wall.

8. Adjust the can so the straw nearly touches the red line.

9. Record the level of the straw in the data chart on the next page for five days. If the straw is pointing to the first line above the red line, write +1. If the straw is pointing to the first line below the red line, write −1. Add a brief description of each day's weather.

Name _____

Barometer Readings

Day	Reading	Weather
1		
2		
3		
4		
5		

Analyze and Conclude

1. What atmospheric factor affects how the barometer works? _____

_____

2. What does a positive reading mean? _____

_____

3. What kind of weather does that indicate? _____

_____

4. What does a negative reading mean? _____

_____

5. What kind of weather does that indicate? _____

_____

6. Observe the readings in your chart. Compare what the readings indicated

with the actual weather in your area. Did the readings correctly reflect the

weather? Explain why. _____

_____

Name _____

Predicting Climates

Read each weather description and predict the type of region and the kind of climate it may have.

1. An area has continual dry weather with very little precipitation.

_____

_____

_____

2. This land region experiences heavy, daily rainfall.

_____

_____

_____

3. This area is a mountainous region located close to the equator.

_____

_____

_____

4. A coastal region is located close to the poles but has warm ocean currents.

_____

_____

_____

Name _____

World Temperature Zones

Label and color in the three major temperature zones. Create your own key using a different color for each zone.

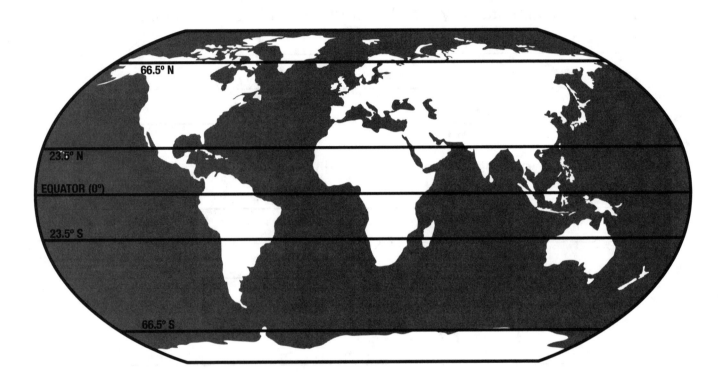

KEY

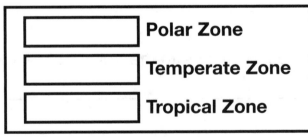

Polar Zone

Temperate Zone

Tropical Zone

Name _____

Vocabulary Review

Write the number of the word that fits the definition on the line in the correct box. If you have matched them all, the sums of the squares in each row, column, and diagonal will be the same.

1. atmosphere	**5.** low pressure	**9.** barometer	**13.** air pressure
2. troposphere	**6.** stratosphere	**10.** absorb	**14.** high pressure
3. climate	**7.** mesosphere	**11.** convection	**15.** temperate
4. ozone	**8.** exosphere	**12.** thermosphere	**16.** cloud

the mixture of gases that surrounds the earth ____	the zone of varying temperatures ____	occurs where cold air sinks ____	absorbs ultraviolet rays ____
the uppermost layer of the atmosphere ____	the layer found above the troposphere ____	the layer where meteoroids are burned up ____	an instrument used to measure air pressure ____
the upper region of thermosphere ____	to take up or take in ____	the transfer of heat in the troposphere by currents ____	occurs where warm air rises ____
the force exerted by air molecules ____	an area's pattern of weather over a long period ____	the layer where weather occurs ____	the suspended droplets of water vapor ____

Name _____

Chapter 11 Review

True – False: Circle T if the statement is true. Circle F if the statement is false. Then change the underlined word to make it a correct statement. Write the new word in the space below the underlined word.

T or F **1.** The <u>stratosphere</u> is where most of our weather occurs.

T or F **2.** When water vapor <u>evaporates</u>, clouds may form.

T or F **3.** Dry climates have low <u>humidity</u>.

T or F **4.** Hail forms inside <u>stratus</u> clouds.

T or F **5.** <u>Wind</u> is formed when air moves from high to low pressure.

Put the layers of the atmosphere in sequence using a 1 for the lowest layer and a 5 for the highest layer.

_____ exosphere   _____ thermosphere

_____ mesosphere   _____ troposphere

_____ stratosphere

List four ways our atmosphere is designed to sustain life.

1._____

_____

2._____

_____

3._____

_____

4._____

_____

Name _____

What makes it noon?

Answer the questions and complete the illustrations below.

1. What time is it? _____

2. What determines the time of day? _____
Illustrate it below.

3. What season is it? _____

4. What determines the seasons? _____
Illustrate it below.

Name _____

Design a Planet

Follow the directions below and use the materials provided to design a planet suitable for your favorite organism.

1. Choose a favorite organism and write its name here: _____

2. Think of all of the things your organism needs to survive. In the lines below, list as many needs as you can.

_____   _____

_____   _____

_____   _____

_____   _____

3. Using the materials provided, design a planet suitable for your organism. Describe your planet below and explain how its design allows your organism to survive. Include your planet's position with regard to the sun, what kind of atmosphere it has, any moons it might have, and what kinds of days and seasons it has.

_____

_____

_____

_____

_____

_____

_____

_____

Name _____

Planetary Motion

Follow the directions below to complete the data table for the experiment.
Answer the questions.

1. Add together all three trials for each string length. Write the total in the
   column labeled Total. Do this for all four string lengths.

2. Find the average for each string length by dividing the Total amount
   by three.

3. To find the number of revolutions per second, divide each Average by 10.

String length	Trial 1	Trial 2	Trial 3	Total	Average	Revolutions per second
100 cm						
80 cm						
60 cm						
40 cm						

1. How does the length of the string affect the number of revolutions?

_____

_____

2. How might this idea relate to the planets revolving around the sun?

_____

_____

3. If you were on a merry-go-round, would you be traveling faster if you sat
   on the outside edge or halfway toward the center? Why?

_____

_____

Name _____

Orbit Shape

Follow the directions below to complete the activity. Describe what you observe and answer the questions.

1. Tie the short piece of string in a circle.

2. Place the points of two pencils on the dots below. Drop the string loop over the pencils. Use the tip of a third pencil to pull the loop outward without moving the first two pencils. With the third pencil, trace the shape that the loop guides you to follow. Repeat this procedure for the second set of dots.

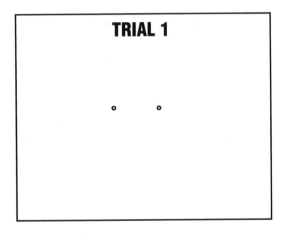

1. What happens to the shape of the ellipse as the two points move farther apart?

_____

_____

_____

2. How does this relate to the shape of satellite orbits?

_____

_____

_____

Name _____

Student Minutes and Light-Years

With your class, develop your own unit of measure and call it *student minutes*. Follow the directions to complete this activity and then answer the questions below.

1. Line up with your group according to your teacher's instructions.

2. When you are given the signal, walk as directed at a steady pace for fifteen seconds.

3. Measure the distance that you walked in meters. Multiply that number by 4 to calculate the distance walked per minute. Record it in the chart below. Repeat this activity two more times.

4. In order to get your average *student minute*, add up your personal results and put that amount in the *Total* column. Divide your total by three to get the *Average* amount and record it. Calculate a *Group Average* by adding all three group members' *student minute* averages and then dividing that number by three.

Names	Trial 1	Trial 2	Trial 3	Total	Average
			Total:		
			Group Average:		

1. How are *student minutes* similar to light-years? How are they different?

_____

_____

2. Do you think that every group has the same average value for *student minutes* as your group has? Why or why not?

_____

_____

Name _____

Labeling Galaxies

Label each galaxy pictured below *spiral*, *irregular*, or *elliptical*. You may use the terms more than once. Then answer the question below.

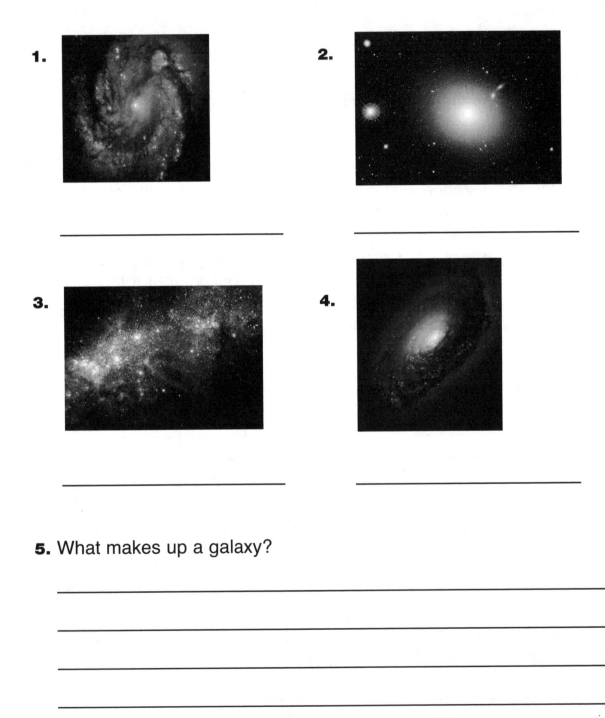

1. _____

2. _____

3. _____

4. _____

5. What makes up a galaxy?

_____

_____

_____

_____

Photos 1, 3, 4, courtesy of NASA and The Hubble Heritage Team. Photo 2 courtesy of CFHT.

Name _____

Making Observations

Look at the two gumdrops that your teacher has provided. In the box labeled *Near*, write as many descriptions as you can of the gumdrop your teacher gave you. In the box labeled *Far*, write as many descriptions as you can of the gumdrop at the front of the classroom. Then answer the questions.

Near	Far

1. Which gumdrop is easier to describe and why? _____

_____

2. Are there any characteristics of the *Near* gumdrop that you can assume
are true of the *Far* gumdrop? Give a few examples and explain why.

_____

_____

_____

3. How might scientists use observations of things in space that are closer to
describe things in space that are farther away? _____

_____

_____

_____

Name _____

Structure Illustration

Illustrate each level of the universe's structure in the boxes provided below beginning with an individual star. Label each level on the lines provided. You do not have to illustrate the universe itself.

1. _____

2. _____

3. _____

4. _____

Name _____

Distances in Our Solar System

Follow the directions below to complete the activity. Fill in the table below and calculate in kilometers the total distance each solar body is from the sun. One sheet of toilet paper is equal to 16,000,000 kilometers.

1. Find the total distance each solar body is from the sun in toilet paper sheets by adding up all of the previous distances.

2. Calculate the total number of kilometers each solar body is from the sun by multiplying your total distance in sheets by 16,000,000.

Name of solar body	Type of solar body	Average distance in sheets from previous solar body	Total distance in sheets from the sun	Number of kilometers from the sun
Sun		Starting point	0 sheets	
Mercury		3.6 sheets		
Venus		3.1 sheets		
Earth		2.6 sheets		
Mars		4.8 sheets		
Jupiter		34.3 sheets		
Saturn		40.3 sheets		
Uranus		90 sheets		
Neptune		101 sheets		
Pluto		86.4 sheets		

Name _____

Color the Distance

Use different colors of crayons or markers to illustrate the relative distances between the solar bodies and the sun. Notice the huge range between Mercury's distance from the sun and Pluto's!

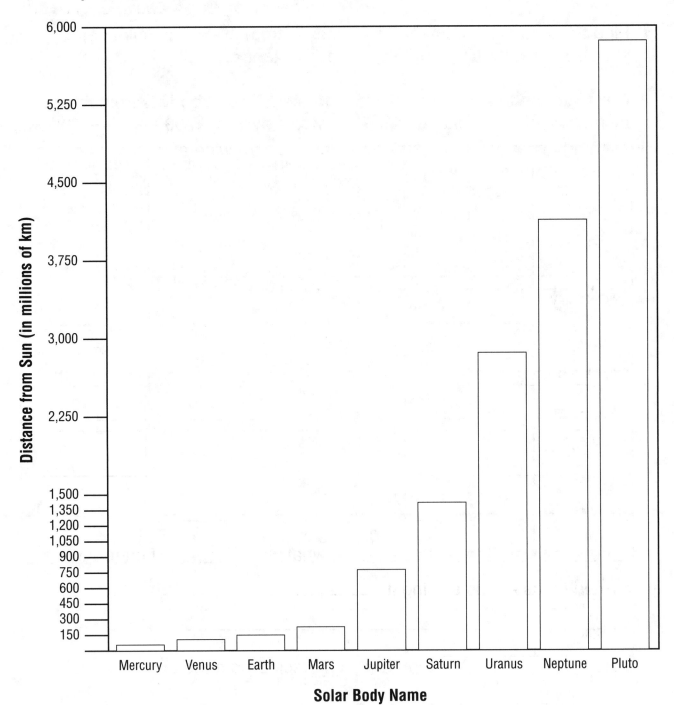

Name _____

Creating Craters

Using the materials your teacher has provided, follow the instructions below to complete this activity. Then answer the questions.

1. Drop your marble onto the sand from a height of 30 cm above the sand. Repeat this twice from the same height.

2. Measure how wide across each crater is. Record each width in the chart below.

3. Smooth the sand using the ruler. Repeat the experiment three times with the marbles at a height of 60 cm. Measure how wide across each crater is and record the widths in the table below.

4. Smooth the sand again and repeat the experiment from a height of 90 cm. Record your data in the table.

5. Find the average width of the craters by adding each of the three trials together for each specific height and dividing by three.

Crater Diameter (cm)				
Drop Height	Trial 1	Trial 2	Trial 3	Average
30 cm				
60 cm				
90 cm				

1. If the sand were the earth's surface, what would happen if craters were

formed by asteroids striking it? _____

_____

2. Why is it important that the earth is protected from the asteroid belt?

_____

_____

Name _____

Our Perfect Position

Read the six items listed below on the left and their descriptions on the right. Draw a line between each item and the description that explains why it is important to the earth's unique design. Answer the question below.

1. observation of the universe

a. The collision distance from Earth is most desirable. Other planets receive more frequent and more damaging impacts.

2. gravity

b. It allows expansion of the universe at a continuous, steady rate.

3. asteroids

c. It produces stronger tides than just the sun would.

4. the atmosphere

d. The position is best within our galaxy. We can look at other galaxies as well as other stars.

5. Earth's moon

e. It has carbon dioxide needed for the greenhouse effect.

6. Is it probable that the earth's position in the universe and all of its other characteristics happened by mere chance? Explain why or why not.

_____

_____

_____

_____

_____

Name _____

Vocabulary Review

Use the vocabulary terms from this chapter to answer the following questions. Write the terms in the blanks provided. When you are done, unscramble all of the letters in the boxes to form a word at the bottom of the page.

1. a huge collection of stars, gases, and dust clouds _ _ _ _ _ _

2. an object that revolves around a larger object in space _ _ _ _ _ _

3. a type of telescope that uses mirrors _ _ _ _ _ _

4. the distance light travels in a year _ _ _ _ _ _ _

5. the principle that states that Earth is designed and positioned for life _ _ _ _ _ _ _

6. all of the matter and energy in existence _ _ _ _ _ _

7. a unit of length equal to the distance between the earth and the sun _ _ _ _ _ _

8. an instrument used to magnify and observe distant objects _ _ _ _ _ _

9. a type of telescope that uses lenses _ _ _ _ _ _

Combine all of the letters in the boxes above to form the word that describes our study of matter and energy in the entire universe:

_ _ _ _ _ _ _ _ _ _ _

© Purposeful Design Science, Level Four • The Universe

12.8B
NOTEBOOK

Name _____

Chapter 12 Review

On the lines below give two examples of instruments scientists use to observe the universe.

1. _____   **2.** _____

3. On the lines below, arrange the following terms in order, from largest to smallest:

galaxy, stars, universe, cluster, supercluster

_____ →

_____ → _____ →

_____ → _____

4. Give an example of a natural satellite. _____

5. What do AUs and light-years measure? _____

6. What is the main difference between reflecting and refracting telescopes?

_____

7. List two ways that our moon benefits Earth. _____

_____

8. What key natural force holds the universe in place? _____

9. List two examples of how Earth has been designed to support life.

_____

_____

Name _____

Feel the Beat

Each time your heart contracts, it pumps blood into your arteries. But, the heart does not pump smoothly like constantly running water. Instead, it pumps blood in a wave, or burst, then relaxes, then pumps another wave, then relaxes. Because of this pumping, the blood does not flow through your arteries smoothly, either. The blood flows in waves that you can feel as a pulse. You can feel your pulse almost any place where a large artery crosses a bone. Two of the most common places to feel your pulse are on your wrist and on your neck. Look at the pictures below to help you place your fingers in the right positions to find your pulse.

Radial Pulse

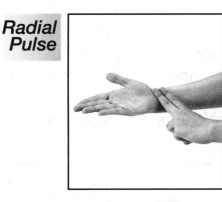

Carotid Pulse

1. After you have found your radial and your carotid pulse, pair up with a partner. One person will be the timer, while the other counts his or her own pulse. Then switch places.

2. Using a stopwatch, the timer will time 15 seconds. Say, "start," when you start the time, and "stop," when you stop the time.

3. When the timer says, "start," begin counting your radial pulse. You may feel two beats occurring closely together. These two beats only count as one beat. Count the beats until the timer says "stop."

4. Record the number of beats. Multiply by 4 and write your answer. This is your pulse rate for one minute.

   Radial Pulse ___11___ x 4 = ___44___

5. Repeat Steps 1–4 for your carotid pulse and record the number of beats.

   Carotid Pulse ___15___ x 4 = ___60___

Name _____

Pulse Rates and Exercise

1. Record your carotid pulse rate from Science Notebook 13.6A in the *Resting* portion of the chart below.

2. Run in place for one minute while your partner times you. Stop immediately and take your pulse for one minute. Record the number on the chart.

3. Sit down right away and have your partner time you as you rest for one minute. After resting for one minute, immediately take your pulse again. Record the number on the chart.

4. Have your partner time you after you rest for three more minutes. Immediately take your pulse for one minute and record it on the chart.

5. Switch places with your partner and repeat Steps 1–4. Answer Questions 1–2.

Resting	_____ beats per minute
After Exercise	_____ beats per minute
1 Minute Recovery	_____ beats per minute
3+ Minutes Recovery	_____ beats per minute

1. Did your pulse increase or decrease after exercise? Why? _____

_____

_____

2. Did your pulse rate increase or decrease after resting for one minute? After three minutes? Why? _____

_____

_____

Name _____

Graphing Pulse Rates

Use the data you collected to fill in the bar graph. Color in each bar with a different color.

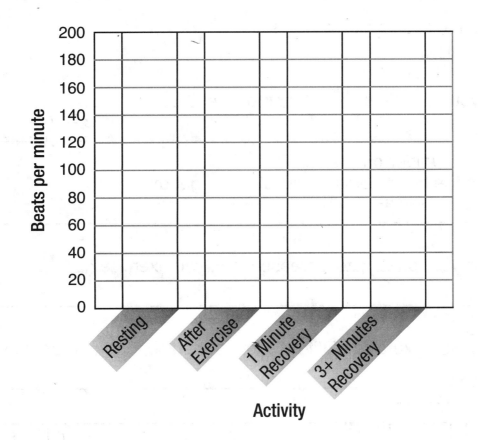

1. Compare your graphed results with three other classmates. Write down

   their names. _____

2. Did their pulse rates increase or decrease like yours did? Explain.

_____

_____

_____

_____

_____

Name _____

Putting It All Together

In order to work properly, muscle cells, like all cells, must have adequate amounts of oxygen. During exercise, the muscle cells demand even more oxygen than usual.

Answer the following questions:

1. How do your muscle cells get their oxygen? _____

_____

2. How does the heart help the muscle cells get oxygen? _____

_____

3. Why does your pulse rate increase when you exercise? _____

_____

4. How long after exercise did it take for your pulse rate to return to the

resting rate? _____

_____

5. Athletes who train often have very short recovery periods. How do you

think you could shorten your recovery period? _____

_____

_____

6. What conclusion can you draw about the relationship between pulse rate

and physical activity? _____

_____

_____

Name _____

A Balanced Diet

The Food Pyramid is an excellent tool to help you make healthy choices in planning a balanced diet. Use the information below to help you plan your meals and snacks for one day.

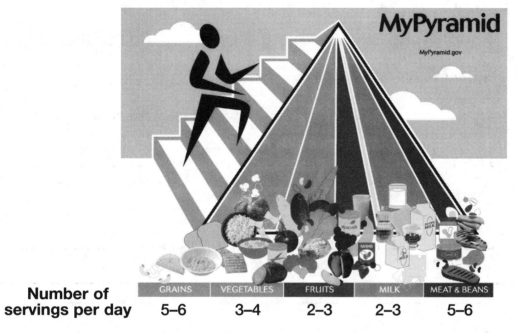

Number of servings per day	GRAINS	VEGETABLES	FRUITS	MILK	MEAT & BEANS
	5–6	3–4	2–3	2–3	5–6

Serving Size Table

Each food group has recommended portions for the equivalent of one serving size.

Breads/Cereals	**Proteins**
1 slice of bread	1 egg
113 g (1/2 cup) rice, cooked cereal or pasta	30 mL (2 tbsp) peanut butter
226 g (1 cup) ready-to-eat cereal	113 g (1/2 cup) cooked dry beans
	28g (1 oz) meat, poultry, fish
Fruits	**Vegetables**
1 medium orange, apple, or banana	226 g (1 cup) raw leafy vegetables
113 g (1/2 cup) chopped, cooked or canned fruit	113 g (1/2 cup) other vegetables
180 mL (3/4 cup) fruit juice	180 mL (3/4 cup) vegetable juice

Dairy
240 mL (1 cup) milk
240 mL (1 cup) yogurt
42 g (1 1/2 oz) cheese

Name _____

My Balanced Diet Plan

Use the *Food Pyramid* on Science Notebook 13.7A to determine how many servings you will need from each food group for one day. Use the *Serving Size Table* to calculate the portions of each food you choose to eat. Also include 60 minutes of physical activities in your plan.

	Food Group	**Serving Size**	**Food Choice**
Breakfast	grians	5 – 6	Cearial
	Milk	2 – 3	eggs
	Meat & Beans	5 – 6	Turkey Bacon
	Grains	5 – 6	pancakes
Lunch	Fruit	2 – 3	Oranges
	Grains	5 – 6	Soup
Snack	Milk	2 – 3	cheese
	Fruit	2 – 3	Bannanas
Dinner	Meats & Beans	5 – 6	Chicken
	Grains	5 – 6	rice
	Vegetables	3 – 4	Salade

Physical Activities _____

_____

13.8A
NOTEBOOK

Name _____

Vocabulary Review

Label the structures in the heart.

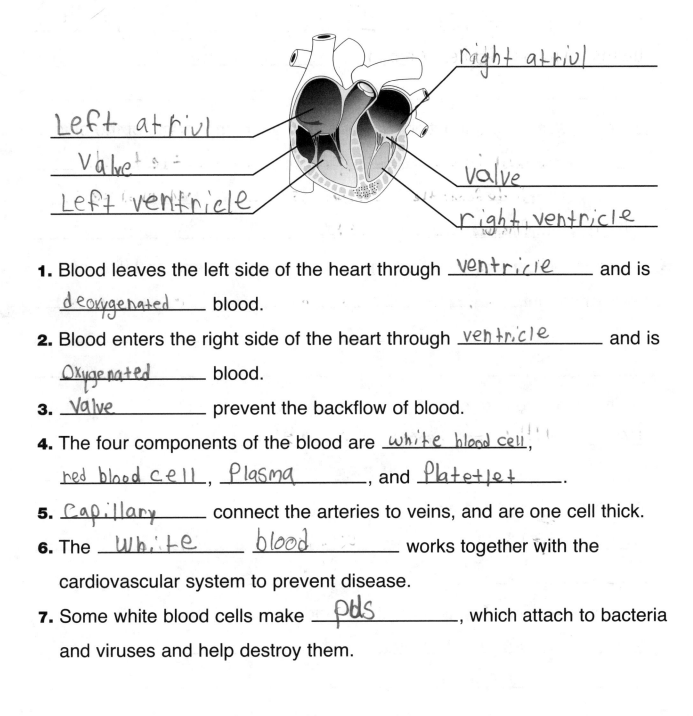

right atriul

Left atriul
Valve
Left ventricle

valve

right ventricle

1. Blood leaves the left side of the heart through __ventricle__ and is __deoxygenated__ blood.

2. Blood enters the right side of the heart through __ventricle__ and is __Oxygenated__ blood.

3. __Valve__ prevent the backflow of blood.

4. The four components of the blood are __white blood cell__, __red blood cell__, __Plasma__, and __Platetlet__.

5. __Capillary__ connect the arteries to veins, and are one cell thick.

6. The __White__ __blood__ works together with the cardiovascular system to prevent disease.

7. Some white blood cells make __pus__, which attach to bacteria and viruses and help destroy them.

Name _Darrin Andrews_

Chapter 13 Review

1. Explain how the three main parts of the cardiovascular system help to deliver oxygen to the body cells. _It carrys the bbod through the veins and to the brain._

2. List and describe the functions of the four main components of the blood. _white blood cell, red blood cell, plasma and platetlet. Whi te blOod cell, it defends the body from diseases. The red bbod cell, it delivers oxygean. Plasma, and Platelets._

3. Describe the barriers your body has that prevent bacteria and viruses from entering it. _antibodies it is made by Porteins made by white blood cells that help destroy bacteria and viruses._

4. List two ways to take care of your cardiovascular system. _Eat healthy to keep the System working_

5. Explain how a vaccine works. _it triggers the production of antibodies._

6. List the three main functions of the cardiovascular system. _The System of vessels and Organs that transports materials around the body._

Name _____

Team Activity Directions

Your team's job is to draw a diagram of the cardiovascular system inside a body outline. Have the team scribe write down the answers to the following exercises.

1. Scribe's name: _____

2. Choose someone to be in charge of noise control. Your team should talk and work as quietly as possible so that you do not disturb other groups (or give away any of your ideas).

Name of noise controller: _____

3. Who are the members of your team?

Members: _____

_____

4. Discuss your plan as the scribe takes notes. What parts must be included on the drawing? What colors will you use? Will you label each part? What resources will you use?

5. Decide how many of you will draw and what parts you will draw. Will you all draw at once or will you take turns? How will you determine what to draw first? How creative will you be? How detailed will your drawing be?

6. What are your observations about the way the students in your team get along? Does your team encounter any problems with the drawing? Is there anything else you or another teammate notices about your team's progress?

7. As a team, choose a group reporter. This person will report to the class about your team's experience. He or she should use the scribe's notes but should also feel free to share his or her own observations.

Name of group reporter: _____

Get busy and have fun!

© Purposeful Design Science, Level Four • Body Systems II

Name _____

Reflecting on the Team Activity

Write answers as your teacher leads a discussion based on these questions.
Write your answers in complete sentences.

1. Did you learn anything new about the cardiovascular system as a result of

having to draw it? If so, what? _____

_____

_____

2. Why was it important for everyone in the group to do his or her part?

_____

_____

3. Did any of the jobs of your group members overlap? If so, give an

example. _____

_____

_____

4. What did your group learn about teamwork? _____

_____

_____

5. Why is the relationship between teamwork among people similar to the

interdependence of the human body systems that God designed? _____

_____

_____

_____

_____

Name _____

Starch Ingestion and Digestion

Follow the instructions on Blackline Master 14.3A. Right after you swallow, answer the questions below.

1. What did the cracker taste like when you first put it into your mouth?

_____

_____

2. What did you taste right after you swallowed the cracker?

_____

3. Was it hard to keep the cracker in your mouth for two minutes?

_____

4. How did you know that the enzymes in your saliva started to break the starch into sugars?

_____

_____

5. The digestive system has four functions. Read the list below. Now state each function aloud to your partner without looking at the list. Then circle the two functions that you just demonstrated:

ingestion   digestion   absorption   elimination

6. Where does digestion of starch begin?

_____

Name _____

Parts of the Digestive System

Label the parts of the digestive system and then fill in the blanks with the correct body organ.

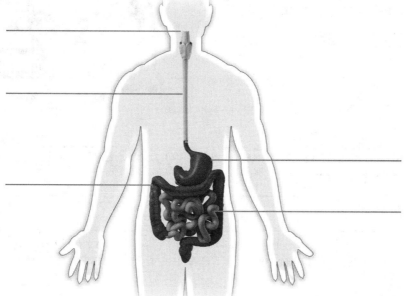

1. This part of the digestive system breaks your food into small pieces and mixes it with saliva. It is the _____.

2. This part of the digestive system mixes the liquid food with acids and enzymes. It is the _____.

3. This part of the digestive system absorbs most of the nutrients in your food. It is the _____.

4. This part of the digestive system connects the mouth to the stomach. It is the _____.

5. This part of the digestive system forms and eliminates the indigestible food particles and other waste products. It is the _____.

Name _____

How do I inhale and exhale?

Based on the Breathing Model you designed, answer the following questions.

1. What does the balloon represent?

_____

2. What does the bottle represent?

_____

3. What does the bag stretched over the bottom of the bottle represent?

_____

4. What happens to the balloon when you push up on the plastic bag piece?

_____

5. What happens to the balloon when you pull down on the plastic

bag piece?

_____

6. When I inhale, my diaphragm _____ _____, causing air to come into

my lungs.

       pushes up   pulls down

7. When I exhale, my diaphragm relaxes or _____ _____, causing air to

move out of my lungs.

       pushes up   pulls down

8. The diaphragm helps the respiratory system. To what body system does

the diaphragm belong?

_____ system

Name _____

Every Breath You Take

Respiration Rate Chart

Resting Respiration Rate	_____ breaths/minute
After Exercise Respiration Rate	_____ breaths/minute

Answer the following questions after you and your partner have recorded your respiration rates.

1. Was your resting respiration rate higher or lower than your partner's?

_____

2. What happened to your respiration rate after exercise?

_____

3. When you exercise, which cells require more energy?

_____

4. When you exercise, which cells require more oxygen?

_____

5. Why do you think your respiration increases after exercise?

_____

_____

Name _____

The Urinary System

Label the diagram with the correct names of three parts of the
urinary system.

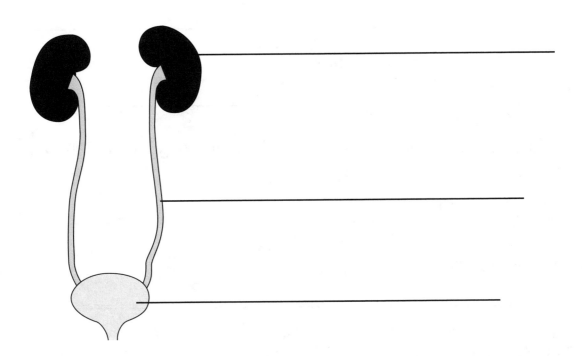

Fill in the blanks with the correct parts of the urinary system.

1. The _____ pass the urine to the bladder.

2. The _____ stores the urine.

3. The _____ filter harmful waste products and excess
salt and water out of the blood, creating urine.

Name _____

The Blood's Filters

After your teacher finishes a demonstration about a filtering process, answer the following questions.

1. What do the green beads represent?

_____

2. What does the red liquid represent?

_____

3. When your teacher poured the mixture through the filter, where did the green beads end up?

_____

4. Where did the red liquid end up?

_____

5. Which organ in the urinary system is in charge of cleaning the blood?

_____

6. Summarize how this organ cleans the blood. You may use your textbook.

_____

_____

_____

_____

_____

_____

Name _____

Recording Vital Capacity

Use these tables to record results from BLM 14.6B.

Data Table A

Trial	Circumference of Balloon
1	_____ cm
2	_____ cm
3	_____ cm

Data Table B

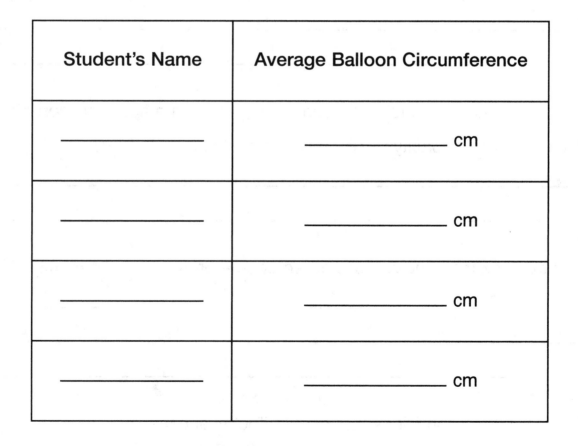

Student's Name	Average Balloon Circumference
_____	_____ cm
_____	_____ cm
_____	_____ cm
_____	_____ cm

14.6B
NOTEBOOK

Name _____

Analyzing Vital Capacity

Answer the following questions. Use the results from Data Tables A and B on Science Notebook 14.6A, along with any other resources you have available.

1. Of the four students, who had the greatest vital capacity? _____

2. Who is the tallest student in your data set? Do you think height might affect vital capacity? Why or why not? _____

_____

_____

3. Asthma is a condition that decreases a person's ability to breathe. How do you think doctors use vital capacity to see if someone has asthma?

_____

_____

4. If you were an astronaut and spent a long time on a space station, do you think your vital capacity would increase or decrease? Why?

_____

_____

5. Do you think that smoking could decrease a person's vital capacity? Why or why not? _____

_____

_____

6. What are three conditions that could affect vital capacity?

_____   _____   _____

Name _____

Sir Hillary's Famous Climb

Read the following paragraphs. Underline facts about Sir Hillary in blue and Tenzing Norgay in red. Circle the ways human bodies can adjust to high altitude.

This New Zealand bill features a picture of Sir Edmund Hillary, one of the two men who first climbed Mt. Everest in 1953. Tenzing Norgay, a Nepalese Sherpa, accompanied Sir Edmund. Mt. Everest in Nepal is the highest mountain peak above sea level in the world. It is 8,850 m (29,035 ft) above sea level. At that elevation, oxygen in the air is less than one-third the pressure of air at sea level. As a result, much less oxygen can cross the microscopic sacs in the lungs to go to the blood and then to the body cells.

The Sherpas are a people group who live in the Himalayan Mountains. There are about 10,000 Sherpas in Nepal. They are traders, using yaks to carry their products down the mountains and returning with goods for the villages. Many Sherpas have also been important parts of climbing expeditions. These people guide climbers, often carrying heavy loads to camps set along the way up the mountain. Sadly, since high altitude climbing is dangerous, many Sherpas and other climbers have died during ascents.

Although Hillary and Norgay breathed oxygen from tanks during their climb, consider what happens to the bodies of climbers who do not carry tanks. First, the climber breathes much faster. This raises the amount of oxygen in the lungs. The body also responds by making more red blood cells to carry all the oxygen possible. If you were to move to a high elevation and live there for a while, your body systems would respond in several ways. Your heart might increase in size so that it could pump blood more efficiently. Your body might even build more capillaries in your tissues to allow more oxygen to pass from your blood to your body cells. People, like the Sherpas, who live their whole lives at high elevations, have bigger chests with bigger lungs.

Name _____

Adjusting to High Elevation

Answer the following questions. Use complete sentences whenever possible.

1. Who are the two men who were the first to get to the top of Mt. Everest? In what year did they accomplished this historical feat?

_____ _____ _____

2. Why do many Sherpas die during their climbs?

_____

_____

_____

3. How do the cardiovascular and respiratory systems work together to help people adjust to higher elevations?

_____

_____

_____

_____

4. Do you think that high elevation can affect vital capacity? Why or why not?

_____

_____

_____

Name _____

Which body system?

Match the body system on the left with its description on the right by drawing a line.

SYSTEM

1. digestive

2. cardiovascular

3. respiratory

4. urinary

5. musculoskeletal

6. nervous

FUNCTION

A. the system that delivers oxygen from the air to the body

B. the system that includes bones and muscles

C. the system that takes harmful substances out of the blood and eliminates them from the body as urine

D. the system that controls your whole body since it includes the brain

E. the system that breaks down nutrients

F. the system that includes the heart, blood, and blood vessels

Which of your body systems is the most interesting to you? Why? You may use your textbook and other resources to write your paragraph. Be sure to use as many vocabulary words from Chapters 13 and 14 as possible.

_____

_____

_____

_____

Name _____

Nutrition, Exercise, and Relaxation Log

Doctors stress the importance of healthy diets, regular exercise, and stress-free living. Complete the personal nutrition, exercise, and relaxation log below for one day. Consider creating a healthy habits journal that you could use every day as you continue to grow.

Date: _____

How much sleep did I get last night? _____ hours

What did I eat today?

Breakfast:_____

  Lunch: _____

  Dinner: _____

  Snacks: _____

Which foods were highly nutritious?

_____

What exercise did I get today?

_____

How long did I exercise? _____ minutes

Did I experience any kind of stress or tension today? If so, what was stressful?

_____

What did I do to relax today?

_____

What could I change or how could I improve my health habits tomorrow?

_____

Name _____

Vocabulary Review

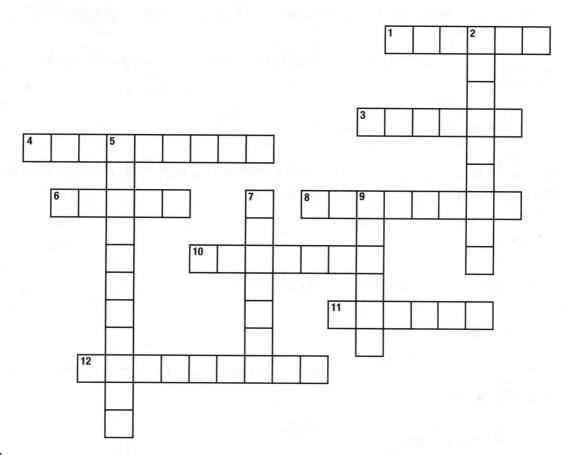

Across

1 a watery liquid in the mouth that usually contains enzymes

3 one of the two organs that filters the blood to produce urine

4 the process of breaking down nutrients into smaller molecules

6 the liquid waste that contains water, salts, and harmful substances

8 referring to the whole person, including mind, body, and spirit

10 the hollow organ that stores urine

11 a protein made by the body cells that helps speed up chemical reactions, such as digestion

12 a muscle that helps with breathing

Down

2 the process of taking food into the body

5 the process of removing wastes from the body

7 the main tube that takes air to and from the lungs

9 the part of the respiratory system that helps make sounds

Name _____

Chapter 14 Review

Read the sentences and unscramble the words to fill in the blanks.

1. _____ refers to the whole of something, like the body, not just the individual parts.

   ichtisol

2. The kidneys _____ the blood, leaving blood cells and nutrients in the blood, but removing waste products.

   rlieft

3. _____ is another word for eating.

   eitonngsi

4. The _____ _____ ingests and digests food, and eliminates food particles.

   devtsieig mssyte

5. Enzymes are used to break your food into small molecules so that they can be absorbed into the blood. This process is called _____.

   netodisgi

6. The _____ _____ allows oxygen to pass to the red blood cells, so it can be delivered to the body cells.

   yoseprriatr mssyte

7. The _____ _____ eliminates waste products and excess water as urine.

   niryuar mssyte